Published in collaboration with the World Wildlife Fund

WILDLIFE '79

The World Conservation Yearbook
Edited by Nigel Sitwell

The Danbury Press

Contributors

John Loudon *President, World Wildlife Fund*

Nigel Sitwell *Advisory Panel, World Wildlife Fund United Kingdom*
Murray McMillan
Janet Coates Barber *Director of Information, World Wildlife Fund United Kingdom*
David Chivers *University of Cambridge*
Philippa Scott
Faith McNulty
Stephen Bolwell
Dr D. A. Burdekin
Eric Eckholm *Worldwatch Institute*
J. J. Cloudesley-Thompson *Professor of Zoology, Birkbeck College*
Michael Freeman
Jon Kenfield
Randall Reeves
Tony and Liz Bomford
David Stonegate

Acknowledgements

2–3 John Barber; 11 Kenneth W. Fink/Ardea; 13 Allan Power/Bruce Coleman; 14 Des Bartlett/Bruce Coleman; 15 Udo Hirsch/Bruce Coleman; 17 Peter Ward/Bruce Coleman; 19 Jen & Des Bartlett/Bruce Coleman; 21 Mary Grant/Bruce Coleman; 23, 25, 26, 27 Murray McMillan; 29 John Barber; 31 Norman Myers/Bruce Coleman; 33 (top) Bruce Coleman, (bottom) Norman Tomalin/Bruce Coleman; 35 Bruce Coleman; 36–7 Barry Driscoll; 38 James Simon/Bruce Coleman; 39 P. Morris/Ardea; 43, 44, 45, 46 Philippa Scott; 49 I. & L. Beames/Ardea; 50, 51 R. F. Porter/Ardea; 53 John Barber; 54 John Borneman (National Audubon Society)/Photo Researchers; 55 P. B. Kaplan/Photo Researchers; 57 Tom McHugh/Photo Researchers; 61, 62 S. Bolwell; 63 (top) C. Balcombe, (bottom) S. Bolwell; 64 Su Gooders/Ardea; 65 Jane Burton/Bruce Coleman; 67 (top) J. D. Bulger/Photo Researchers, (bottom) Su Gooders/Ardea; 68 Bob Gibbons/Ardea; 69 (top) John Sims/Bruce Coleman, (bottom) Leonard Lee Rue/Photo Researchers; 71 Rouxaime/Jacana; 73 (top) Hans Namuth/Photo Researchers, (bottom) Carré/Jacana; 75 Su Gooders/Ardea; 77 (top) Hans W. Silvester/Photo Researchers, (bottom) Bernard Mallet/Jacana; 79, 81 Clem Haagner/Ardea; 82–3 collection Varin-Visage/Jacana; 84 Jen & Des Bartlett/Bruce Coleman; 87 (top) Hans & Judy Beste/Ardea, (middle) J. L. S. Dubois/Jacana, (bottom) Jos Van Wormer/Bruce Coleman; 88, 89, 91, 92 Michael Freeman; 95, 96, 97, 98, 99, 101, 102–3, 104–5 Jon Kenfield; 107, 109 Leonard Lee Rue/Bruce Coleman; 111 Francisco Erize/Bruce Coleman; 113, 115, 117 Tony & Liz Bomford; 119, 121 (top) Inigo Everson; 121 E. Mickleburgh/Ardea; 122 collection Varin-Visage/Jacana; 123 Francisco Erize/Bruce Coleman; **Cover** Jacana

First published in the United States of America in 1979
by The Danbury Press, a division of
Grolier Enterprises Inc.
Publisher: Robert B. Clarke

ISBN: 0-7172-8124-8
Library of Congress Catalog Card Number: 78-71968

© London Editions and
World Wildlife Fund International 1979

This book has been designed and produced by
London Editions Ltd.,
30 Uxbridge Road, London W12 8ND

Printed in Spain by TONSA - San Sebastián. 1979
Depósito Legal: S. S. 252 - 79

While it is intended that the information and opinions
expressed in this book reflect the policies of the World
Wildlife Fund and its sister organization, the
International Union for Conservation of Nature and
Natural Resources, the contents are the responsibility of
the various contributors and the editor.

CONTENTS

FOREWORD
John Loudon
President World Wildlife Fund International

We in the World Wildlife Fund are often asked why we try to save so many endangered species. Here is a fairly typical comment: 'Many little-known species could surely be allowed to vanish without any noticeable ecological effect. Doesn't it make more sense to concentrate on the important ones, or those which have a really good chance of survival?'

Despite a steadily rising income, our available resources are still pitifully small compared with what we need to spend on conservation. It does indeed make sense to concentrate on areas where we can achieve the maximum benefit. Nevertheless, we have always believed that the wildlife conservation movement should try to save as many threatened species as it possibly can.

The World Wildlife Fund and its scientific advisory organization, the International Union for Conservation of Nature and Natural Resources (IUCN), possess both the will and the skills needed to solve many of the world's conservation problems. And we know that they can be solved, with generous public support.

The IUCN has prepared 'A World Conservation Strategy', at the request of the United Nations Environment Program (UNEP). This is basically a plan of action for the years ahead. I am sure that this immensely important document, which was jointly published by World Wildlife Fund and UNEP, will mark a significant turning point in attitudes and conservation efforts around the world.

INTRODUCTION
Nigel Sitwell

A little while ago I was discussing the text of a proposed charter for nature with a group of dedicated and knowledgeable conservationists. Little time was spent arguing the merits of the actual words of the draft: curiously, however, more attention was devoted to whether or not the charter was necessary at all. I say curiously, because one might have supposed that professional conservationists would be the first to welcome an international declaration of this sort – a kind of Declaration of Wildlife Rights.

One view was that there were already enough words written about conservation, and a few more would hardly make any difference. Another was that the time has passed when such a document would have much practical value. Ten years ago, perhaps twenty, an international expression of concern for the environment would have made an impact (and indeed several such declarations have been made over the past two or three decades, and have become enshrined in the conservationist creed). But now, so the argument ran, most people know that conservation is necessary; they do not need to be reminded in flowery language of its importance.

It is true that many people do now recognize the desirability of conservation, but I wonder to what extent this is simply an abstract concept which these same people find difficult to apply to the practical business of everyday life? Or, more likely, prefer to ignore when it proves inconvenient?

Kenya is on the whole one of the most conservation-minded countries in Africa, and is keenly aware that its rich wildlife heritage is a source of considerable revenue from tourists. On the other hand, individual members of parliament in Kenya are reported to have expressed some very unconservationist sentiments in a recent debate. Crocodiles, said one MP, were of no value to the tourist industry and the large numbers in Lake Victoria were a menace. He added that it was not important to conserve hyenas as they were 'very ugly animals' and tourists were not interested in them. Another speaker suggested that the government should not be seen to protect animals more than its citizens, and that creatures like porcupines and wild pigs should be eradicated or confined to 'animal orphanages'.

Although the economic benefits of wildlife-based tourism are certainly a good argument in favour of conservation, it does not follow that animals of minor interest to the tourist have no useful role. (And anyway, it is clearly not true that tourists don't want to see crocodiles and hyenas, as many of them definitely do.)

The debate in Kenya seems like a case of short-term economic self-interest overshadowing more general considerations. Another example of the same kind of thing cropped up on the other side of the world, in New Zealand, where the Minister of Lands gave permission for clear-cutting of North Island's last remaining habitat for saddleback and blue-wattled crows. These semi-flightless birds need to climb trees in order to launch themselves into the air, a fact which the minister overlooked when replying to a protest by the Royal Forest and Bird Society. Since both species were protected by law, he said, the loggers 'won't be allowed to harm the birds'. Did he really not know that the birds actually needed the trees? Or was he simply being rather naive? Or was it that he was merely trying to find an excuse with which to mollify the conservationists?

'A little learning,' said Alexander Pope, 'is a dangerous thing.' He might well have been referring to ecology, for the one thing the ecologist learns, as he learns more, is the impossibility of knowing everything – and the importance of what he does not know. Ecology may be defined as the study of the interrelationships of living things, and the paradox is that the better these patterns are understood the more complex they are seen to be. It also becomes obvious that all living things are to a greater or lesser extent inter-dependent, and that the chances are slender of correctly predicting the consequences of interfering with these dependencies.

While it is true that the more we know, the more we find that we do not know, it is also true that the more we know, the better off we should be. However, there are some things which are difficult if not impossible for us to find out directly – for example, the squids which are eaten by sperm whales. David Stonegate notes in his article that whales, birds, and seals in the Antarctic consume about 20 million tons of squid every year, but this is only a proportion of the worldwide total. British marine biologist Malcolm Clarke reckons that overall sperm whales alone eat about 100 million tons of squid, or nearly 50 per cent more than the total annual catch of all types of fish.

Squid populations are clearly very important in the marine ecosystem but about the only way we can find out much about them is to examine the stomach contents of sperm whales. Dr Clarke hits on the core of the problem: 'Let us hope that the public's enthusiasm for a moratorium on sperm whale killing is matched by the enthusiasm of biologists and whalers to collect samples from stomachs in all regions where whaling is still going on. If that is not done we may find it impossible to make even the broadest estimate of some squid populations which are inaccessible to us.' Speaking for myself, I hope that the whalers do not take up this line of reasoning in order to justify the continuation of whaling at present levels. They have already claimed that were it not for whaling we would know very much less than we do about whales. This may be true,

but it is cynical to pretend that it is a good reason for catching large numbers of whales – to the extent that several species are near extinction. A similar argument is used by other hunters to justify their activities. In Britain, for example, where the otter is now greatly reduced in numbers, otter hunters have defended their sport on the grounds that most of the facts about otters come from them and if they were not allowed to hunt, a valuable source of information would disappear. This spurious argument did not carry the day, however, and otter hunting is now banned in England and Wales (though not in Scotland, where otters are more numerous).

Ideally, discussion of the pros and cons of conservation should be removed altogether from the arena of economics and vested interests. Perhaps we should pay heed to the words of Jimmie Durham, a Cherokee Indian who is director of the International Treaty Council. 'In the language of my people,' he told a US government committee, 'there is a word for land: Eloheh. This same word also means history, culture, and religion. We cannot separate our place on the earth from our lives on the earth nor from our vision or our meaning as a people. We are taught from childhood that the animals and even the trees and plants that we share a place with are our brothers and sisters.'

Referring to the proposed Tellico Dam project of the Tennessee Valley Authority, which would have flooded the valley behind the dam and destroyed the habitat of a fish called the snail darter, Jimmie Durham said:

The flooding of our old valley has been stopped temporarily because of a little fish that lives there and nowhere else. Many people have made fun of this little fish and I would like to ask why it is considered so humorously insignificant. Because it is little, or because it is a fish? This incredible arrogance towards other life has caused great destruction in this country. To me, that little fish is not just an abstract 'endangered species', although it is that. It is a Cherokee fish and I am its brother. Somehow, it has acted to save my holy land so I have a strong gratitude for that fish.

MEETING THE CHALLENGE
World Wildlife Fund Report

The World Wildlife Fund's principal campaign at present is for conservation of the seas and marine life. This is of paramount importance because it is to the seas to a very large extent that we look to provide food for our rising numbers. But at the same time we are poisoning the continental shelves, which are the main fishing areas, with pollution from factories and cities and with oil spillage, thus reducing their productivity. Over-fishing has led to drastic reduction in catches of some popular fishes such as herring in the North Sea, or haddock on the United States Atlantic coast. Many sea animals are threatened with extinction because of pollution and over-exploitation.

Saving the whales

The plight of the great whales has undoubtedly touched public imagination more than that of any other creature. The blue whale, which can grow to 100 feet long and weigh over 150 tons, is the largest animal known to have lived on this earth. In half a century whalers slaughtered some 300,000 and only in 1965, when the number was so small that they were scarcely worth hunting, was it agreed to give them full protection. Other great whales – the fin, the humpback and the bowhead – have been reduced to commercial extinction, and there are grave fears for the future of the sperm, Bryde's, sei and minke whales. The World Wildlife Fund continues to press the International Whaling Commission for the ten-year moratorium on whaling which was approved by the United Nations General Assembly in 1972, but so far the whaling countries – principally Japan and the Soviet Union – have rejected the proposal.

Meanwhile projects have been going ahead to save the whales. An important advance was achieved when Maui County Government proclaimed a reserve for the humpback whale between December and May when they gather in local waters to mate and calve. This was a direct result of a World Wildlife Fund research project on the humpbacks led by American scientists Dr Roger Payne and Dr Sylvia Earle.

Dr Payne is a leading expert on the curious 'songs' of the humpbacks which have so intrigued scientists and the general public. These songs are common to whole populations of humpbacks, and they change through the mating and calving season. Although the whales do not sing in their Arctic and Antarctic feeding areas, they resume each new season at the point they left off. But even now the purpose of the songs has not been established nor even whether it is the males or females who sing them.

Studies have also been going on of Inuit (Eskimo) hunting of the curious narwhal, in which species the males grow a long projecting spiral tooth. These teeth were produced as proof of the existence of the unicorn in medieval Europe. The Inuit hunt the narwhal mainly for its flesh, which is known as *muktuk*, and not for the ivory tooth. But there is a natural tendency to go for well developed males because the ivory can be profitably sold. It is hoped to work out suitable conservation regulations with the participation of the Inuit and the Canadian authorities.

A new potential threat to the whales, and to other Antarctic species, including seals, seabirds, fish and squid, is the harvest

While the killer whale is not
threatened with extinction, some
of its larger relatives are.
And some dolphins and porpoises
(on which the killer whale preys)
are also under pressure

of krill, which is starting in the Southern Ocean. Krill are small shrimp-like crustaceans. They are found in hundreds of millions and are the main food of the great whales. They are now looked upon as the world's largest potential source of animal protein. In order to provide guidelines for controlling exploitation the World Wildlife Fund is financing a study by the International Institute for Environment and Development of the political and economic aspects of the krill harvest, while a parallel project involves the construction of a mathematical model of the Southern Ocean ecosystem in order to predict the effect of various krill harvesting regimes, in particular on the whales.

The threat to coral reefs

Another form of exploitation of marine resources which is potentially damaging is the extraction of coral sands, which are used for building purposes. Coral reefs and lagoons are important environments for future economic development and their marine life represents renewable natural resources on which many islanders depend. Apart from destruction of dredged zones, drifting clouds of small particles choke and silt nearby coral communities. Research is being carried out in French Polynesia and the French Antilles so that controls may be proposed which will give guidance on areas for exploitation and technical means of limiting pollution of surrounding areas.

Affluence and air travel have brought many virtually pristine coral seas within range of tourist divers. Uncontrolled use of spearguns and underwater breathing apparatus is leading to impoverishment of coral and related fish communities. The World Wildlife Fund has constantly urged governments with such tourist areas to ban the use of spearguns and ensure the conservation of reef communities. The Sudanese Red Sea reefs have become a popular diving place for Europeans, and the World Wildlife Fund provided the services of a scientist who prepared diving regulations, located good diving areas where moorings were provided to obviate damage to reefs from anchors, and publicized the value of the reefs. It was found that sailors on ships waiting to enter Port Sudan were raiding the reefs with pickaxes and crowbars to collect corals as well as speargun fishing. The Sudanese authorities cracked down heavily on offenders, who were rapidly brought to justice and fined.

The Palau archipelago, 300 miles east of the Philippines, is considered to be one of the most beautiful coral atolls in the Pacific. But combined American, Iranian and Japanese interests have proposed to develop it into a super oil port and storage area with ancillary petro-chemical industries. The consequences for the Palauans and their environment, as well as for a number of unique species, could be severe, if not disastrous. The World Wildlife Fund is providing funds for an independent study in order to inform the Palauans of the ecological effects and the options open to them for alternative economic development.

The threat to Palau is a particularly dramatic modern development, but other oceanic islands are suffering from the effects of long-term mismanagement of the environment and over-exploitation. Unique island species are often unable to compete with introduced species, or to defend themselves against predators such as cats, dogs, pigs and rats. In the Seychelles, the magpie robin is one of the world's most endangered species. Only thirty-nine were found to survive in 1977 on Frigate Island, their last sanctuary. A large part of the indigenous vegetation has gone, but it is hoped to recommend land use practises which will ensure the robin's survival. However, so as not to keep all the eggs in one basket, six robins were moved to the island of Aride, where it appears that they are settling down well.

Coastal marshes and wetlands

Fringing the seas are coastal marshes and wetlands, which are important habitats for birds and fish and many other forms of life. Often regarded as useless wastelands fit only for dumping and reclamation, they are in fact some of the most biologically rich areas on earth. Many fish spend part of their life cycles in estuaries and coastal marshes, and destruction of such habitats can have devastating effects on commercial fisheries. The Wadden Sea, a shallow inland sea along the coasts of the Netherlands, Denmark and

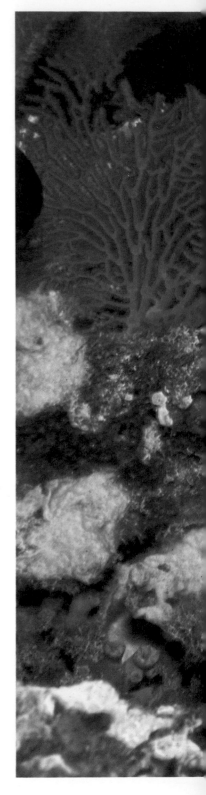

Coral reefs are incredibly rich natural habitats, but they are fragile – biologically as well as literally – and are easily destroyed. They can be choked by drifting silt, and even pulled to pieces by the anchors of fishing boats

Germany, is a prime example. A high proportion of the North Sea fish stocks depends on the health of the Wadden Sea, which is also the resort of hundreds of thousands of birds and seals. And yet this area is deluged with pollution from northwest Europe's industries, and the land is reclaimed for industry and subjected to intense tourist pressure. The World Wildlife Fund continues to support work in all three countries, having jurisdiction for the conservation and rational use of this valuable area.

Many of the birds which visit the Wadden Sea migrate along the Atlantic coast of Europe to Northwest Africa and here one of the key areas is the Banc d'Arguin, an area of islands, shallow lagoons and tidal mudflats off the coast of Mauritania. This is where the Sahara meets the Atlantic and the bird fauna of Eurasia mixes with that of Africa. After several years of preparation the Government of Mauritius formally inaugurated the Banc d'Arguin National Park in June 1978. The World Wildlife Fund has supplied equipment and specialist assistance for the park, which is also a haven for the endangered Mediterranean monk seal.

The survival of the oryx

The Arabian oryx is believed to be extinct in the wild; but the first steps have now been taken to reintroduce this beautiful white antelope to its native deserts. In February 1978 four young male oryx were flown from San Diego Wildlife Park in California to the Shaumari Wildlife Reserve in Jordan, where facilities have been established for captive breeding. Later, four females were flown out to join the males. But it will be several years before release takes place into the wild, probably not until the third captive generation at Shaumari.

The return of the oryx to Arabia was a momentous occasion for the World Wildlife Fund, for one of the first projects it supported was an expedition sponsored by the Fauna Preservation Society of London and the IUCN, which captured three oryx in what is now South Yemen. They were flown to Phoenix Zoo, Arizona, and with animals donated by the Sultan of Kuwait and the late King Saud they formed the basis of the so-called 'World Herd', which by 1978 had grown to some 120 animals.

The expedition to capture wild oryx was mounted as a last-minute bid to save the Arabian oryx from extinction. For centuries the Bedouin had hunted the oryx, for to kill one was a sign of manhood. It was indeed an achievement in former days when only a camel and primitive weapons were available. But after World War II all-terrain vehicles became available, as well as powerful weapons, and the oryx were systematically hunted down by motorized fleets of hunters. By 1960 it was apparent that the oryx, which had once roamed through most of the Arabian peninsula, was doomed unless urgent action was taken.

Some oryx did survive in the desert, and an expedition in Oman in 1974 found three dead and evidence that four had been captured by pursuing vehicles, believed to have come from outside Oman. They may have been the last wild oryx.

The captive breeding facilities at Shaumari in Jordan have been established with World Wildlife Fund assistance, including the provision of an expert to plan and supervise the work. Meanwhile plans have gone ahead to reintroduce oryx also to Oman, where the Wadi Yaluni in the Jiddat al Harasis has been chosen as the most suitable place. This is near where the oryx were captured in 1964 and offers good security under the supervision of the Government of Oman.

The Arabian oryx is almost certainly extinct in the wild, but one of the first World Wildlife projects was to capture some specimens in what is now South Yemen, and establish the 'World Herd' of captive oryx in United States zoos. Four animals have now been returned to the Shaumari Wildlife Reserve in Jordan

Though the wildlife of the Galapagos Islands enjoys a relative lack of natural predators, and is thus quite tame, some creatures are now threatened by introduced domestic animals, such as feral dogs. Among these threatened species is the land iguana, and so attempts have been made to breed it in captivity; in June 1978 the first-ever captive-bred land iguana broke out of its shell at the Charles Darwin Research Station in the Galapagos

Galapagos land iguana hatched in captivity

The Galapagos land iguana is one of the unique species which gave Charles Darwin inspiration for his theory of evolution. He saw the iguanas, along with varieties of giant tortoises and finches, during a brief visit in 1835. Even then the threat to these animals, which had evolved in a completely natural way, was developing. Passing ships put goats ashore and settlers brought with them pigs, dogs and cats. Rats inevitably moved in too. All these introduced species played havoc with the indigenous animals, which had never had to face predators and competitors before. Among the species which suffered was the land iguana, and it became extinct on several islands.

In 1976 it was discovered that feral dogs had started to attack hitherto untouched iguana populations and the Galapagos National Park Service and the internationally-supported Charles Darwin Research Station launched a rescue operation. They brought survivors to the station and set out to breed them. This was a difficult business, for little was known about their breeding biology. Conditions closely resembling those in the wild were created in corrals and early in 1978 four females laid eggs. Mr Howard Snell, the scientist in charge, placed the eggs in several experimental incubation systems in order to determine which would yield the highest percentage of hatching success. On 5 June, after 110 days' incuba-

tion, the first Galapagos land iguana ever hatched in captivity broke out of its shell, which had been in a plastic bag placed in a solar incubator. The jubilant scientists nicknamed it 'Charlie'.

In the wild the Park Service guards continued their long battle to bring under control, and preferably eliminate the feral dogs.

Rescuing threatened species

The oryx story is a good example of one of the major facets of the World Wildlife Fund's work – the saving of species from imminent extinction. This often involves 'fire-brigade' actions like the rescue of the oryx, followed by captive breeding to build up numbers, while efforts are made to ensure suitable protected habitat for reintroduction in the wild in due course.

Several species are in this critical situation, including the Mauritius kestrel, the Waldrapp ibis, and the Galapagos land iguana. In all these cases there was good news in 1978.

The Waldrapp ibis is a black bird with a bald red crown. It once nested in many parts of Europe, including the Jura, the Alps and the Danube basin, as well as in Asia and North Africa. While a few hundred still nest in Morocco and Algeria, the last Eurasian nesting site is at Bireçik on the banks of the Euphrates, near Turkey's border with Syria. At Bireçik the ibises have long nested on a cliff face in the middle of the village, but in recent years buildings have closed in on the cliff, and there has been increasing disturbance during the breeding season. In addition the use of pesticides on crops where the ibises feed is believed to have affected their breeding success. In 1953 some 1,300 ibises nested at Bireçik, but in 1978 only thirteen pairs nested. For several years the World Wildlife Fund had been doing its best to help by improving the nesting ledges, building artificial ones, and encouraging local people to protect the birds, but despite this numbers continued to dwindle.

In 1977 the Turkish authorities decided that an attempt must be made at captive breeding, as well as to try to persuade the ibises to change their nesting site. Two adult birds and nine young were taken into captivity, and a large aviary was constructed against a suitable cliff about a mile from Bireçik. When it was ready the captive birds were put into the aviary with the hope of attracting the incoming migrants.

The signs are that the trick will work. Some birds from the old colony visited the aviary and sat beside it. Two of them flew up to artificial nesting sites and behaved like a mated pair, giving hope that they may use the site next year. Meanwhile the pair in the aviary produced two chicks. More chicks were taken from the wild so that the captive colony could be built up and made even more attractive as a nucleus for 1979's breeding season.

Far away in the Indian Ocean lies Mauritius, where a unique falcon teeters on the brink of extinction. This is the Mauritius kestrel and in 1974 only six survived, two of them in captivity, where it was hoped they would produce young. So far the breeding experiment has not achieved satisfactory results, but meanwhile the wild kestrels seem to be saving themselves. One of the principal reasons for the drastic decline of the Mauritius kestrel, apart from destruction of its habitat, was that monkeys, which had been introduced to the island, raided the nests and ate eggs and young. By a fortuitous chance in 1975 one of the last two wild pairs chose to nest on a rock face where the monkeys could not reach the site. Three young kestrels fledged successfully and became the first to survive to maturity for at least two years. By 1977 three pairs had nested on the cliff face and raised seven young.

We may in fact be witnessing evolution in progress for, as Dr Warren King, of the International Council for Bird Preservation, which is managing the project, commented: 'If the preference for cliff nest sites is learned by the new chicks, the kestrel's chances for survival will improve vastly.'

More protection for elephants
In May 1978 the United States Government placed the African elephant on its list of threatened species. This followed an intensive enquiry to which a major contributor was Dr Iain Douglas-Hamilton, who is leading the World Wildlife Fund/IUCN Elephant Project, which has been in opera-

tion for three years. The listing means that trade in ivory or other African elephant products will be strictly controlled and thus provides additional protection to the species, which is declining throughout most of its range. Dr Douglas-Hamilton estimates that there are at least 1,300,000 African elephants, but on his reckoning known exports of ivory from Africa in 1976 may have amounted to anything between 100,000 and 400,000 elephants, which gives some idea of the threat to the species. A survey in Kenya indicated that the elephant population there had been halved in five years.

The Asian elephant is also the subject of increasing attention. It is in greater danger than the African. It is estimated to number between 27,000 and 40,000 scattered from the Indian subcontinent through peninsular Southeast Asia and Sumatra. In this heavily populated area clashes between elephants and humans continue to increase, and demand great efforts to work out ways in which they can live together.

Tigers – ups and downs
Operation Tiger, the World Wildlife Fund's overall campaign for conservation of the big cat throughout its range in Asia, went into its sixth year with good progress reported in most areas. India and Nepal led with their comprehensive government programs covering thirteen reserves, where good protective measures have been put into effect, and scientific management of the habitat is going on. In Nepal's Chitawan National Park, Nepalese and American scientists are capturing tigers with tranquillizer guns and putting radio collars on them in order to record their movements and behaviour. A substantial base of information has been built up over four years which will help in the management of tiger and other wildlife in the inevitably small areas that are likely to remain to them in this world crowded with humans.

The situation of the tiger in Indonesia is not a happy one. Three forms existed there on the islands of Bali, Java and Sumatra. The Bali tiger has been considered extinct for several years, but recent information suggests that it might survive in remote parts of the island and a new search is planned. Likewise there have been fresh

Wildlife cannot survive without suitable habitat, so much effort is being made to conserve suitable areas as national parks. Rain forest is especially vulnerable – and under pressure. Some 40 per cent of the original forest has already been destroyed, and it is being cut down at the rate of fifty acres a minute

reports of Javan tigers which require investigation. The only known survivors are four or five in the Meru Betiri reserve in eastern Java. The Sumatran tiger probably numbers about 1,000, and is still illegally hunted. But the World Wildlife Fund has been helping the Indonesian authorities to find suitable reserve areas, as well as seeking sterner action against poachers.

Digit the Mountain Gorilla murdered

Saddest news of 1978 was of the killing of Digit, a mountain gorilla in Rwanda's Volcanos National Park. Digit had become famous in films showing his gentleness with American scientist Dian Fossey, who had been studying him for eleven years since he was an infant. Poachers cut off his head and hands to sell. A few months later two other gorillas of Ms Fossey's study group were slaughtered. With fewer than 500 mountain gorillas surviving, the loss is tragic both for the species and for science. The President of Rwanda informed the World Wildlife Fund that three of Digit's killers had been imprisoned and others implicated were being pursued.

Digit's death highlighted the serious problem of exploitation of wildlife for tourist souvenirs and luxury decoration. In many countries where local people had only mildly exploited the local fauna and flora, the advent of tourists willing to pay locally astronomic prices for souvenirs, has encouraged grossly excessive hunting. The situation had become particularly bad in Kenya, where the wealth of wildlife attracts such numbers of tourists that the income vies with coffee as the principal foreign exchange earner. Worldwide financial instability helped to provoke rises in the price of ivory leading to massive poaching of elephants – the population was halved between 1973 and 1977 – while even common species, such as zebra, suffered noticeably in numbers as they were killed for their skins. In 1977 the government cracked down on licensed hunting, and in 1978 a ban on trade in wildlife products came into effect. These moves were widely applauded by the conservation community, including the World Wildlife Fund, which had long been urging such action.

World-Conservation Strategy

While there is drama in these rescue operations the real battle is to achieve the conservation of our whole natural environment on this earth. Neil Armstrong, the first man on the moon, told the World Wildlife Fund Congress in London in 1970:

> To stand on the surface of the Moon and look at the Earth high overhead is certainly an unique experience. Although it is very beautiful it is very remote and apparently very small. We have all been struck by the simile to an oasis or an island. More importantly, it is the only island that we know is a suitable home for man. The importance of protecting and saving that home has never been felt more strongly.

Even with the great development of nature conservation in recent years efforts have been piecemeal and inadequate to meet the challenges posed by the human population explosion and the overwhelming power of modern technology over nature. The year 1978 may be a watershed. After long months of work by leading scientists and other experts all over the world the International Union for Conservation of Nature and Natural Resources, the WWF's scientific partner, produced a World Conservation Strategy. Commissioned by the United Nations Environment Programme (UNEP), and financed by UNEP and the World Wildlife Fund, the strategy provides, for the first time, a global perspective of the many problems with which conservation is concerned and a means of ranking the most effective solutions to the priority problems. It is aimed at all governments and other concerned organizations, international and national, official and non-official, so that they can coordinate their efforts and avoid duplication.

Nature conservation is not a luxury in which only wealthy nations and individuals can indulge themselves. Far from it. It is in fact a matter of life or death for all, including the poor and developing countries. It is a vital part of economic development.

The World Conservation Strategy points out that lack of conservation is resulting in reduction in fertility and often the outright destruction of vast areas of productive land. Major fisheries are being depleted and the ecosystems on which they depend are being degraded. There is a staggering loss of

The African elephant is declining in numbers throughout most of its range. In Kenya a recent survey indicated that the number may have halved in the past five years. The chief cause is poaching for ivory and other elephant products.

species and varieties of plants and animals, many of which hold the key to high food yields, progress in the struggle against disease, and the generation of new products to meet human needs and raise the quality of life. Degradation and depletion on such a scale directly threaten the survival and well being of many peoples and the stability of their governments.

The strategy document proposes the management of human use of the biosphere, and of the ecosystems and species that compose it, so that they may yield the greatest sustainable benefit to present generations while maintaining their potential to meet the needs and aspirations of future generations.

The production of the World Conservation Strategy is undoubtedly the most important work that the IUCN has ever undertaken. But it has always played a major role in promoting conservation of nature and natural resources and has been the World Wildlife Fund's scientific adviser. Financial support for the IUCN has been a World Wildlife Fund priority, along with two other key organizations – the International Council for Bird Preservation, which is the principal international specialist organization in its field, and the International Waterfowl Research Bureau, which coordinates work on swans, geese, ducks, waders, coots, and flamingos and their wetland habitats.

Conserving habitat

All efforts to save endangered wildlife will be of no avail unless the habitat remains, and thus the establishment of conservation areas such as national parks or nature reserves is a major aim of the World Wildlife Fund. Since its foundation in 1961 it has helped the establishment, expansion and maintenance of conservation areas all over the world totalling over 520,000 square miles – an area equal to France, West Germany, Italy and the United Kingdom combined or twice the size of Texas. This is nearly one per cent of the world's land area.

In recent years there has been a special effort to achieve the establishment of national parks in areas of tropical rain forest, and assistance is being given to countries in Latin America, West Africa

and Southeast Asia. The threat is a very serious one, for 40 per cent of the original 6,370,000 square miles of this richest of all the world's environments has been destroyed and the rest is being felled and burned at the rate of fifty acres a minute. These forests have been traditional sources of food, medicinal products and timber, and their potential value to human life is enormous but barely explored. Their destruction is a major tragedy of our time.

In order to inculcate conservation ethics among young people the World Wildlife Fund has continued to aid the World Scout movement in its international program. Aid has also gone to Wildlife Clubs in Africa and Asia. A special mention is due of the Wildlife Clubs of Kenya, which celebrated its tenth anniversary in 1978. From an initial group of twelve clubs it has grown to a nation-wide movement with 550 clubs with a membership of about 27,000.

In 1978 World Wildlife Fund aid to conservation since its foundation topped $35,000,000. But this amount is not a measure of achievement, for judicious use of funds as seed money and counterpart funds, plus the use of high-level influence on governments and other authorities, has obtained results incalculable in financial terms. Nevertheless the task ahead demands far, far more and the World Wildlife Fund, working in cooperation with all devoted to the conservation of nature, intends to meet the challenge.

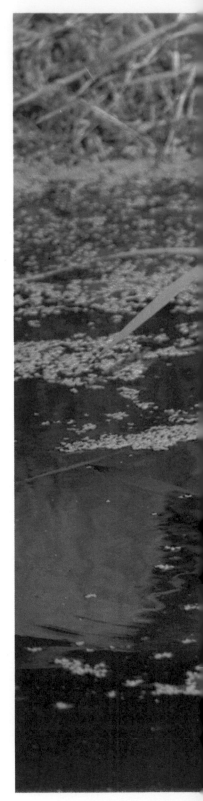

Operation Tiger, the World Wildlife Fund's campaign to save the tiger from extinction, went into its sixth year with good progress in India and Nepal. However, the tigers in Indonesia and some other areas are still severely threatened

CONSERVING KOALAS
Murray McMillan

The koala is rarely seen in the wild in Australia, and almost never seen outside Australia, even in zoos. This is not because the species is rare or in danger of extinction, but because of the very sophisticated environment which it needs in order to survive.

Exact estimates of the number of koalas are not available, but surveys have assured conservationists that the species is not threatened. In March 1976 experts from all over Australia met at Taronga Zoo, Sydney, for a symposium on koala management, biology, and medicine. After two days of talks they agreed unanimously that the koala was neither rare nor in danger of extinction. But, they concluded, the vulnerability of the koala to environmental factors such as overgrazing, disease, or fire nevertheless emphasized the need for active conservation management.

The koala was under threat in the early part of the twentieth century when it was hunted for its skin. But the commercial exploitation of this lovable and harmless animal raised such a public outcry that the koala today is, if anything, overprotected. This overprotection is having its own adverse effects on man's ability to manage the species' conservation. One of the organizers of the Taronga symposium, Thomas John Bergin, a veterinary scientist and at that time the curator of mammals at Taronga Zoo, says that overprotection of the koala has led to it becoming one of the least studied of the Australian marsupials.

There is a complete ban in Australia on the exploitation of koalas, and this ban has been applied to zoology as well as commerce. It has inhibited scientific studies which would have provided valuable information to conservationists concerned about the animals' future. But following the Taronga symposium, researchers have found wildlife authorities a little more agreeable to requests for research animals.

The Taronga symposium proceedings are reported in a book, *The Koala*, published in June 1978 by the Zoological Parks Board of New South Wales. Mr Bergin, the book's editor, said that almost all systematic studies of the koala had been carried out through government departments, and until the symposium the fragments of knowledge about the animal had never been gathered together. 'It seemed timely to find out where we stood and which studies were most needed in order to base the future conservation of the koala firmly upon scientific knowledge,' he said. 'Accordingly, the first Taronga symposium was convened and to our gratification over forty people having first-hand knowledge of some aspect of koala biology were brought together.'

Mr Bergin said papers presented at the symposium showed how much had been learned in recent years, but also how little was known. 'The koala's fastidious food preferences, for example, remain far too complex to be understood with our present attitude and techniques ... Its digestive processes, and the role of micro-organisms in them, need much more study. Koalas have been bred in captivity, but only rarely, and the factors determining success or failure have not been clarified.'

Diet and digestion are but two of the specialized problems facing conservationists dealing with the koala. 'Koala' is

Though once threatened because of the demand for its fur, the koala today is neither rare nor in danger of extinction. It is, however, still vulnerable, and needs to be scientifically managed

an Australian Aboriginal word meaning no water, and koalas will not drink water except in rare circumstances.

The animal lives in the eucalyptus trees which are native to Australia, and the eucalypt's leaves are its sole diet. But of more than 500 varieties of eucalypt, the koala will only eat a limited number – some experts say about fifty. Of these, only twenty to thirty provide the koala's staple diet. The remainder provide only occasional browsing.

A Sydney researcher, Stephen John Cork, of the Department of Zoology at the University of New South Wales, is studying the koala's digestive system and hopes to discover the quantity of leaves that it needs to consume. Mr Cork's research has shown that a koala takes two weeks to pass only half a meal through its digestive system, and up to two months for the entire meal to be excreted. He believes that the fibrous diet of eucalypt leaves requires this long digestive process. Eucalyptus oil is also highly toxic to animals and humans, and the process of detoxification could require a longer digestive time, and may also represent a drain on the animal's energy supplies.

Stress is another of the main problems in the management of koalas, and causes a number of deaths following relocation of the animals from habitats which have become overcrowded. In an effort to find the reasons Dr Bruce Alan Scoggins, of the Howard Florey Institute of Experimental Physiology and Medicine at the University of Melbourne, is conducting research into the koala's adrenal steroid production.

The acting chief of the Division of Wildlife Research of the Australian Commonwealth Scientific and Industrial Research Organization (CSIRO), Dr John Henry Calaby, says that the CSIRO's observations in Australia's eastern states confirm that koala numbers give no cause for alarm. The government wildlife services of the states of Queensland, New South Wales, and Victoria monitor koala communities and so keep a check on the status of the species.

In one of the Taronga symposium papers, biologists Ian Harvey Eberhard and Rodney J. Pearse say that koalas today are

A mature female koala produces one young each year, and looks after it to the end of its first year. Young koalas mature faster than the older animals die, so the maturing animals are obliged to disperse; their survival depends on whether they can find suitable habitat

found in eucalypt forests from North Queensland to Victoria. Most populations are of low density, but there is a scattering of high-density populations. In their paper they say that they believe the distribution of koalas has changed little in a hundred years but that numbers have declined, mainly due to loss of habitat but also because of exploitation, disease and bad management. 'Koalas are in no danger of extinction but many dense populations are threatened and will require active management for their conservation,' say the two biologists.

Koalas live in 'islands' of suitable habitat, and if these become too crowded there is a tendency for the animals to overgraze and destroy their own food source. 'The koalas' strategy for survival is based on a stable adult population in good habitat whose members are long lived. Each mature female produces one young per year and successfully raises it to the end of its first year.'

Eberhard and Pearse agree that adult koalas are faithful to their home range, so when this becomes overcrowded immature adults are forced out to find their own habitat. The rate at which koalas mature far exceeds their rate of mortality, so maturing adults are forced to disperse. 'Survival depends on whether the dispersing koala can find suitable unoccupied habitat.' The authors add that koala conservation programs should involve protection and management of both animal and habitat. Koala populations in good habitat could provide maturing koalas each year to create new colonies in other unpopulated but suitable areas. They recommend that wildlife authorities release more animals for research, particularly if the results are likely to benefit management.

The conflicting needs of the researchers, and the care of the wildlife authorities to protect koalas, concern Ronald Strahan, a research fellow at the Australian Museum, Sydney, and a former director of Taronga Zoo. He says that the koala has been given unique protection.

Indeed, the protection is so great that we have, on occasions, been faced with mass deaths in populations of koalas

Koalas feed entirely on eucalyptus leaves, though only about fifty varieties out of 500 are suitable, and some twenty to thirty provide the animal's staple diet. 'Koala' is an aboriginal word meaning 'no water', and the koala rarely drinks. The degree of protection which the koala receives in its native Australia is occasionally the cause of disaster. Populations can increase in particular areas to such an extent that mass deaths result through lack of food

which have reproduced to such an extent as to eat almost all the available food in an area. Even in stable populations there is insufficient food and space. One of the continuing problems of koala management is the transfer of animals from areas of high population. Unfortunately, our knowledge of the basic biology and diseases of koalas has so many gaps that such transfers often fail inexplicably. Because of the virtually complete protection of the species it is extremely difficult to conduct the sort of research that would resolve many of the management problems.

Dr Michael Leonard Braysher, a wildlife biologist with the conservation and agriculture section of the Australian Government's Department of the Capital Territory, has had first-hand experience of the vulnerability of koalas to environmental forces. He is in charge of a koala research program at Tidbinbilla Nature Reserve, about twenty-four miles from Canberra, Australia's national capital; koalas were reintroduced to suitable habitat in the reserve in 1969.

The colony is currently thriving and supplying researchers with much information on the koalas' social organization, but success came only after an initial tragic failure. Dr Braysher, who joined the program in 1974, reports that of the sixteen koalas first transferred to the colony, only one survived. The cause of these early deaths is uncertain, though Dr Braysher believes it could have been a combination of stress and wasting disease. He says that the koala's new habitat had the right varieties of trees, and the trees had an abundance of leaves. But eucalypts, after a drought, withdraw protein from their leaves – often twelve months after the drought has ended. The Canberra district suffered a bad drought in 1968. The Tidbinbilla koalas ate well and always had full stomachs, but they still died. 'They were eating,' says Dr Braysher, 'but I don't think they were getting enough protein.'

WILD ASSES
Janet Coates Barber

The world's wild asses have always seemed to inspire much less excitement than other members of the horse family. Zebras, for example, are seen by millions of tourists in Africa and, instantly recognizable, they have over the years provided the standard 'Z' picture in children's alphabet books the world over. Their skins are exported, regrettably, to appear as floor coverings, as purses, or as telephone directory covers, in many countries. For this reason, they occupy a place in the contemporary concern of conservationists involved in improving international trade controls for threatened species. There is probably cause for concern for the future of all zebras. (Even the now extinct quagga – a kind of brown, partially striped 'zebra', once found in southern Africa – has aroused more interest than the asses, because of its curiosity value.)

The world's most endangered wild horse, now almost certainly extinct in the wild, is Przewalski's horse. This animal has interested the public, although it has been seen by very few people. It is found in one of the most romantically uncomfortable places in the world. Living in the high, sparsely vegetated semi-desert of Mongolia, whipped by gales, snow, and sandstorms, Przewalski's horse has had a hard time surviving.

People think of wild asses as uninspiring relatives of the long-suffering domestic donkeys – the epitome in the animal kingdom of oppressed and resentful submission. Domestic donkeys are in fact very intelligent and not always as patient as their reputation implies. And scientists who have worked with asses in the wild have been very

impressed by their tremendous powers of endurance, their speed, intelligence, wild independence, and, surprisingly, their grace.

The domesticated donkey is descended from one or several of the African wild ass races, and has been in the service of man for much longer than the horse. In spite of its down-trodden demeanor, it has had its moments, as G. K. Chesterton so vividly points out in his defiant poem 'The Donkey':

The tattered outlaw of the earth,
    Of ancient and crooked will;
Starve, scourge, deride me: I am dumb,
    I keep my secret still.

Fools! For I also had my hour;
    One far fierce hour and sweet:
There was a shout about my ears,
    And palms before my feet.

The African wild asses are considered the most intelligent of the horse family by some scientists. The Nubian and Somali wild asses are both likely contenders as the ancestor of the donkey.

The Nubian race may now be extinct, but once occurred in the mountainous semi-deserts of Nubia and eastern Sudan from the Nile to the Red Sea. It is smaller than the Somali race (about 43 to 48 inches at the shoulder, i.e. 11 to 12 hands high). It has no leg stripes but a well-marked shoulder cross. The Nubian wild ass, probably rare at the beginning of this century, was even then fully protected by law from hunting in the Sudan (along with, at that time, the 'zebra, ostrich, shoe bill, ground hornbill, secretary bird'). However,

The kiang, one of the two races of northern wild ass, is now protected by the Chinese government, and although numbers are low it does not seem to be in any immediate danger of extinction

it could be exported live for a license fee of ten Egyptian pounds.

The Somali wild ass is about 50 inches at the shoulder (i.e. 12.2 hands high) and has well-marked leg stripes but no shoulder cross. It is found in northern Somalia, where about 250 may survive, and used to be found well into Eritrea to the point where the Ethiopian highlands meet the sea, and south into the Ogaden. The same race is also found in the Danakil Depression in north-eastern Ethiopia. There is some uncertainty as to whether a third race does exist – an unusually small and rather dark wild ass with leg stripes and a strong shoulder stripe. Such animals have been seen in Eritrea, but are now believed to be hybrids produced by domestic donkeys and Somali wild asses.

The World Wildlife Fund supported a research project on the Somali wild ass in 1970, which revealed that although legally protected in Somalia and Ethiopia this race is still under great pressure. Only 2,000 to 3,000 survive, in spite of the fact that most of the areas where they live are semi-deserts with little potential for human beings and their stock. In the Danakil, which is a stony depression 400 feet below sea level, the temperature can reach 122°F (50°C) in the daytime.

One of the main continuing threats to the African wild ass is the pressure imposed by the Affar and Issa tribes, who still hunt them for meat. The Koran recommends the eating of ass meat, which is believed to hold hepatitis and other diseases at bay. The shooting of the animals may not have great impact in normal times, but when drought affects herd numbers anyway, shooting has an increased effect, particularly as stallions, often standing apart from the main group, get shot most frequently. Also, in other areas, domestic stock compete with the ass for grazing and water, which is in very short supply.

The asses are shy and wary and will generally take rapid flight at the approach of humans. Their hard hooves enable them to clamber or sprint up very steep surfaces. This ability is badly needed, to avoid one of the most unnecessary pressures they have to suffer. In more populated areas tourists chase the asses in cars to photograph them,

pursuing them until they collapse with exhaustion. This is now a major cause of ass mortality. Dizzying circles on the ground woven by vehicles relentlessly harassing the asses can be seen from the air, and are an appalling indication of human stupidity and insensitivity. Many recommendations were made as a result of the WWF survey, some of which were implemented; a Danakil National Park now seems possible to protect asses in that area.

In Asia, wild asses occupy rather different habitats from those utilized by the wild asses of Africa. However, all the equine characteristics, including a keen sense of smell and hearing, the use of kicking and biting as defensive actions, a hardy resilience and wildness (only worn down by the pressures imposed by man), are all present, and are necessary for plains and semi-desert species.

The asses of Asia are more dependent on water than those of Africa, and although the Asian races are adapted to drinking salty water, unless even this is available in adequate quantities when required, they cannot survive. Wild asses were once one of the most populous ungulates in Asia, but numbers have been declining for 2,000 years and are now lower than they have ever been. Separate populations of different races are constantly in retreat from human interference, and also drought. Hunting, as well as disease introduced by domestic stock, has certainly played a part in their decline.

As with the African asses, there is some confusion about the number of races that may exist and the names given to them. Also as in Africa, there are feral populations which probably represent mixtures of several different races. It is believed that Asiatic wild asses have never been domesticated, but have crossed with domestic horses.

The kiang is said to have been crossed deliberately or accidentally with horses in Tibet. This, the biggest of the wild asses, is the most 'horse-like' of the various races. Some scientists believe it differs sufficiently from the others to justify its being considered as a separate species. It can measure 56 inches at the shoulder (or 14 hands). It has a long, upright mane and a pronounced

The Somali wild ass (seen here in the Hai-Bar Reserve, in Israel), is one of two African races of wild ass. About 250 may survive in the wild in northern Somalia. It is a likely contender as the ancestor of the domestic donkey

black back stripe. In summer its coat is a clear, bright red, and in winter it is long, thick, and browner.

The kiang is found at heights up to 15,750 feet on the Tibetan plateau; it is fully protected by the Chinese, and although numbers are low, it is not believed to be endangered. Wolves prey on herds and pick up new-born foals. Kiangs live in groups of five to ten animals and even as many as 400. Their lips and mouths are adapted to eating tough, unappetizing vegetation, of which they take advantage during the short steppe summer in August and September. At this time they put on a considerable amount of weight to help them get through the cold and drought of the fiercely rigorous winter. They break ice to reach water, and snow also helps to satisfy their needs. Kiangs have been seen assembling in herds of 1,000 and provide a stirring sight, particularly in flight as they stream away in a single file. In summer they cross rivers – a 'bathing' experience which they seem to relish. In spite of the well-organized and disciplined social structure of the herds, there is an absence of what might be called closeness between individual animals, and physical contact is most likely to take place during fierce mating or fighting.

The Dziggetai is the second of the northern ass races, living now only in southern Mongolia (and possibly in Sinkiang, China, where it is also protected). Again, herds of up to 1,000 have occasionally been seen. It is one of the bigger asses with a shoulder height of 46 to 53 inches (or 11.2 to over 13 hands). The Russian zoologist Professor Andrei G. Bannikov has reported that there may be 15,000 in Mongolia, where the habitat is slightly more congenial than in Tibet.

The Syrian race of the Asiatic wild ass is probably extinct but may occur in a remote and uninhabited region just north of the Syrian-Turkish border, between Aleppo and Mosul. It is unlikely that it does survive, and hunting by Bedouin tribesmen is said to be a major cause. This is the smallest of the wild asses (39 to 40 inches, barely 10 hands), and may once have been found in southern Turkey through the Middle East to Iran.

The most threatened of the surviving Asiatic wild asses is undoubtedly the Indian wild ass, or khur. It is smaller than the northern asses, reaching a maximum of 50 inches (or 12.2 hands). Numbers have declined from about 3,000 to 5,000 in 1946 to under 400 today. It is still unprotected, and although like most other asses it has been pushed into less than suitable habitat (described as 'salt encrusted desert') it nevertheless still has to compete with domestic stock. It is found in the Little Rann and possibly the Great Rann of Kutch in the Gujarat-Pakistan border region where seasonal flooding by the sea leaves no forage except on grassy hillocks.

The khur was once found over a wider area in the dry regions of north-west India and west Pakistan. Many factors have led to its unhappy decline. Drought has encouraged livestock owners to use marginal areas which otherwise would not have been grazed, leading to conflict with the asses. Diseases (among them African horse sickness) have been introduced and are weakening the herds. Hunting and the capture of foals were once a considerable pressure, but less so now. Apart from competition for grazing, planting of parts of the habitat with the African babul tree – an aspect of a government forestry program – is decreasing their range still further. The establishment of a military camp has not helped either. It has been clear for some time that protection for the Indian wild ass is urgently required, and a proper survey must be carried out to estimate its numbers and distribution.

The remaining wild asses have attracted a number of common names and definitions as to race, depending on where they are found. The onager of Turkmenia is sometimes referred to as the kulan (which is the name applied to the wild asses found in Iran), but some scientists have given these animals the name Ghor-Khan. There is, however, definitely a population of wild asses in Turkmenia, Soviet Central Asia, whether one calls them kulans or onagers. There are reputed to be about 1,200 of them in the Bad Khyz reserve, where they are well protected. Another population lives on an island in the Aral Sea known as Bausa Kelmes ('place of no return'). While

all asses move very swiftly, the kulan or onager is particularly fleet. It can reach speeds of about forty miles per hour over short distances, and can maintain speeds of nearly thirty miles per hour over long distances; it can therefore easily outpace a horse.

The wild ass of Iran also has a reputation for being swift-footed and tireless. It is protected there, and about 1,500 survive in reserves, although hunting is still believed to take place. These asses have been referred to as 'the pathetic remnants of the huge herds that once migrated back and forth across the great Persian deserts up into the high desert valleys in summer and down into low-lying areas in winter.' The places where they live match only the habitat of the kiang for severity of climate. Summer temperatures reach 136°F (58°C) in the Iranian desert, which is devoid of trees and other cover, and most other wild animals and plants.

These underrated, neglected, but unexpectedly inspiring animals merit much more attention and interest than has been afforded them so far. Wild asses have done their best to retreat from areas of conflict with humans, but survival is proving difficult for most of the races, in Africa and in Asia.

The kulan (above) is found in Iran and numbers about 1,500 in reserves. It is fleet of foot and endures a severe climate, with summer temperatures reaching 136°F in the desert. The onager (right) hails from Turkmenia in Soviet Central Asia. These names are rather confusing, and the words 'onager' and 'kulan' are often interchanged

GIBBONS IN DANGER
David Chivers

The lesser apes or gibbons are found throughout the mainland and islands of Southeast Asia. They are almost wholly arboreal and live on fruit and leaves; they have a spectacular arm-swinging form of movement, and pure, distinctive but complex calls that can be heard at considerable distance. The different species and sub-species vary in colour, markings, and calls but all have long arms, no tail, dense hair covering, and an upright posture. In most species the face markings are particularly attractive and it is their endearing expressions, along with their gentleness, intelligence, and docility that make them among the most appealing of primates. Indeed, their very attractiveness is one of the factors contributing to their threatened existence.

It has been estimated that less than 4 per cent of gibbon habitats are currently protected as forest areas, national parks, or game reserves. Given the present rate of forest clearing for timber or farming, and of hunting for food and both local and export trade, 80-90 per cent of gibbon populations will be wiped out within fifteen to twenty years, with the extinction of one, if not more, species and the survival of the remainder in isolated forests. Thus, the gibbon is an endangered species and although most gibbon populations are at the moment healthy current trends must be halted or reversed if they are to remain so.

There are nine recognized species of gibbon. The siamang, a black ape, is twice the weight of the other gibbons and is found in the mountain regions of Sumatra and peninsular Malaysia. The concolor, also known as the crested or white-cheeked gibbon, occurs in Laos, Vietnam, Hainan, and South China. Its calls are very high-pitched and pure in tone. The hoolock is also known as the white-browed gibbon and is found in Assam, Burma and Bangladesh. The kloss gibbon is black like the siamang but smaller and is restricted to the Mentawai Islands off West Sumatra. The pileated (capped) gibbon is found in southeast Thailand and Cambodia; the male is black with white hands, feet, and head-ring, while the female is silvery gray with black chest and cap. The gray gibbon varies in color from mouse-gray to brown with black on the cap and chest and inhabits all but the south-west part of Borneo. The silvery gibbon is now found only in the western half of Java and its estimated population of several hundred is in serious danger of extinction. The agile or dark-handed gibbon is found in three populations – firstly, in the Malay Peninsula; secondly, over all but the north of Sumatra; and thirdly, in south-west Borneo. The lar, also known as the white-handed gibbon, is also found in three populations – over most of Thailand; most of peninsular Malaysia; and North Sumatra.

All gibbons live in monogamous family groups of an adult male and female and several dependent offspring, and all live in territories from which others are excluded by loud calls accompanied by gymnastics. All species eat only fruit, flowers, or leaves. Gibbon territory sizes differ, however, from species to species depending on varying feeding habits. The siamang, for example, lives in a territory of twenty hectares. This is less than half the size of the lar gibbon territory but nearly twice the size of the

One of nine recognized species of gibbon, the silvery or moloch gibbon is now found only in the western half of Java in Indonesia. Its estimated population of a few hundred is seriously endangered

Seven of the nine species of gibbon: top row (from left to right) – lar, kloss, and hoolock; bottom row – gray, dark-handed, siamang, and concolor

kloss gibbon territory. The siamang spends about 80 per cent of its time in the central half of its territory where three-quarters of of the food trees are situated. It is thus relatively sedentary. By contrast, the lar gibbon feeds less than the siamang and travels widely through its territory, foraging here and there for food but converging to eat with its family about two or three times a day. The smallness of the kloss gibbon territory is probably due to their island isolation and to threats from man. It is significant that they are the only gibbons to have two calls which are used solely in encounters with man. Understanding and respect for such territorial differences is essential in any conservation program. Without it, the different species will not survive.

The main threat to the gibbon population throughout Southeast Asia is the continuing clearance of forests for timber and farming land. Even where forests have only been partially cleared the delicate ecological balance necessary for the gibbon's survival is alarmingly disturbed. While fruit trees and others may not be felled, sleeping and rest trees are often removed. Moreover, increased sunlight alters the vegetation and climate of the forest, and many of the food trees necessary to gibbons thrive only in dark, moist conditions. At the moment at least half of the land area is being cleared or partially cleared in gibbon-inhabited countries.

In Assam, the home of the hoolock gibbon, there are no forests which are officially protected. Indeed, large tracts of virgin forest are being fully cleared, and in the few forest reserves where the hoolock still occurs, partial deforestation is being carried out without any consideration for the needs of the gibbon population. As a result, groups are becoming increasingly isolated. Suggestions have been made for a hoolock gibbon reserve, but so far no action

The white-cheeked gibbon is sometimes known as the Indo-Chinese gibbon. It lives east of the Mekong River in Laos and Vietnam, where it is probably endangered. Its distinctive facial appearance sets it apart from any other gibbon

has been taken.

In Thailand, the threat is three-fold: the destruction of forests for timber and farming land; hunting; and the demand for gibbons for pets or for research. Commercial exploitation of forests all over the country goes on and this is aided by the building of new roads to the more remote areas. Slash-and-burn farming techniques mean the irreversible destruction of forested land. Recent legislation has banned both the hunting of gibbons and the export of gibbons for pets or research. The latter measure has been relatively successful, although some smuggling still occurs. Hunting for food or pets, however, continues unabated. Another recent move has been the preservation of several large forest areas as game reserves or parks (although the forested mountains on the Malaysian border where agile gibbons are found remain unprotected), and with full protection and control these could support healthy

The white-handed or lar gibbon is found over most of Thailand, most of peninsular Malaysia, and north Sumatra. It is probably about the most numerous of all the gibbon species

gibbon populations. There is, however, some fear for the pileated gibbon in southeastern Thailand, where only one suitable area is protected. Other possible habitats are being rapidly destroyed. The conservation of wildlife has become a public issue in Thailand but it now remains to be seen whether the worthy legislation carried through can actually work, particularly in a country where bribery, corruption, and exploitation are everyday realities.

In Malaysia the problems are similar, although hunting is not quite so widespread and export controls seem to be effective. Here, however, the forests are cleared not so much for farmland but for industrial development. Hydro-electric schemes are being constructed in lowland forest areas (the most suitable habitat for gibbons), and it has been estimated that in the one half of the forest remaining in the peninsula, forest clearance is being carried out at the rate of 2,500 square kilometers per year. This could mean that in ten to fifteen years only 4,000 gibbons might remain here. To the credit of the Malayan Nature Society and the Forest Department, proposals have been put forward which link economic development with the conservation of natural resources. Of the 83,362 square kilometers of forest in the peninsula the Forest Department hopes that more than 50,000 square kilometers will be set aside as permanent forest. This would include not only reserve areas for gibbons but also 'productive' forest, scientifically developed and controlled for the supply of timber and other produce.

If such a plan were carried out by these efficient departments healthy populations of siamang, lar, and agile gibbons would continue to thrive even if other forest is cleared. Similar conservation efforts are being carried out in East Malaysia and in Sarawak. The Forest Department is particularly concerned with the conservation of all primates and has set up several projects to assess current population sizes and distribution, to establish suitable reserves, and to develop rehabilitation centers to return confiscated apes to the wild.

In Indonesia some positive moves have been made to protect gibbon populations, although here as elsewhere clearing of

A lar gibbon. The main threat
to the survival of all gibbon
species is forest clearance, and
even where forests have been
partially cleared, the ecological
balance may have changed
alarmingly as far as the gibbons'
needs are concerned

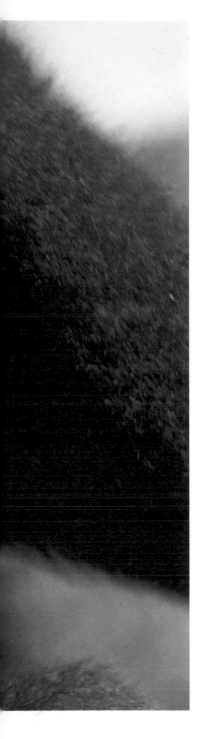

forests has been and still is a major threat to these lesser apes. The fate of the rare moloch gibbon of Java remains in the balance and unless some effort is made immediately the remaining few hundreds of this species will die out. In Borneo particularly the clearing of forests for timber goes on apace and there are, as yet, few reserves. Gibbons are protected throughout Indonesia but it is really only on the Mentawai Islands that conservation is extensive. The Teitéibatti Wildlife Reserve in central Siberut covers sixty-five square kilometers of forest and will soon be extended to a hundred square kilometers. The four islands support 50,000-80,000 gibbons and have been selected as an area for special attention by World Wildlife and Survival International.

In the long term, however, integrated projects aimed at conserving wildlife while at the same time helping human activity must be set up. These two considerations are not as incompatible as they at first seem. Already UNESCO, through their Man and Biosphere (MAB) program, are urging the establishment of reserves on the sites of existing national parks while taking into account man's economic needs. They suggest that an inviolate core, where wildlife can flourish undisturbed, should be surrounded by a buffer zone, where limited but valuable human activity can take place. Such activities would include environmental studies and research, some degree of land management, and tourism. It is inevitable that large areas of forest must be cleared and devoted to human use, but also some areas must remain untouched if wildlife is to survive. It has been suggested that 50 per cent of forested land should be cleared for human activity, 20 per cent reserved exclusively for wildlife, and the remaining 30 per cent managed carefully. It is important to realize that the benefits from such a program are mutual. The preservation of forests is essential to man's survival in that the full extent of the resources of the forests has not been clearly understood or exploited by man; forests control the flow of water and sediment to populated lowlands; and forest soil, particularly in hilly areas, is not suitable for sustained farming.

It is particularly important to bear in mind that gibbons are a territorial species and that the needs of the nine species differ. They do not readily adapt to a changed environment as has been proved in Indonesia where homeless gibbons have been captured and transferred to other forested areas with very limited success. For the same reason they cannot be preserved in captivity in significant numbers. Conservation of large tracts of forest is therefore the only answer to the survival of gibbon populations.

At the moment the healthiest gibbon populations are the siamang, lar, agile, and gray, but the silvery, some races of concolor, and perhaps pileated, might well be extinct within a decade. The kloss is also threatened and lack of information on the hoolock is cause for alarm. Action is urgently needed, particularly in Java, Indochina, and Thailand, to set up suitable reserves and to enforce bans on the exporting of gibbons, but all of the countries of Southeast Asia must adopt a long-term policy of conservation if the gibbon is to survive. International pressure and publicity is useful in drawing attention to the possible fate of the lesser apes and efforts by wildlife organizations are of great importance. However, unless the governments and the local people in the countries concerned become increasingly aware of the need for conserving gibbons – through education and involvement – all other efforts will be in vain.

RED BREASTED GEESE IN ROMANIA

Philippa Scott

On 9 December 1968 two ornithologists, Heinz Hafner from Germany and Hayo Hoekstra from Holland, reported an amazing spectacle of an estimated 500,000 white-fronted geese and 25,000 red-breasted geese in a huge field south of the Danube Delta between Constanţa and Tulcea.

The main breeding ground of these beautiful little red-breasted geese is in Arctic Siberia in the area of the Taimyr peninsula and most of their migration is within the USSR. At one time, earlier in the century, their autumn migration took small numbers of them through Hungary and Czechoslovakia, but now, due to habitat changes and heavy hunting pressure, the Dobrogea area of the Danube Delta seems to be the only remaining part of their range outside the USSR. Where they go after December in a severe winter is still not known for certain. We have been told that very few now frequent their former wintering grounds on the shores of the Caspian. Because of his special interest in these geese, my husband (Sir Peter Scott) set out with Dutch ornithologist Tom Lebret at the end of November 1969 to visit the area of the Hafner/Hoekstra sightings of the previous year. Accompanied by Professor Valerius Puscariu from the Romanian Academy of Sciences they hired a car in Bucharest and drove to Constanta, and from there went in search of the geese. This is rolling country with wheatfields and maize stubble in the winter months, the individual fields being anything from 100 to 1,500 acres; there is practically no cover.

It is an agricultural scene. Small villages with mud roads, here and there a huge

Red-breasted geese breed in Arctic Siberia and migrate mostly within the Soviet Union. They also travel to the Danube Delta in Romania

collective farm and tractor station. In 1969 conditions were very primitive and travelling and accommodation were a considerable problem. However, during the six days they were there the party found the geese and by crawling into a small quarry on their stomachs through muddy plowed fields in the rain, on one day they were able to get reasonably close to a flock of 4,000 redbreasts with 3,000 whitefronts. This was the largest concentration of redbreasts they saw.

In November 1971, I was one of a party of four who visited the area again. Also looking for the geese in the same area were another group of ornithologists, so we were able to pool our information. Morning flight each day was something of an adventure. The drive from Tulcea (where we stayed) to see the morning flight was about forty miles and sometimes more. The weather was frequently very cold, with severe frosts, snow, fog, or rain. The traffic on the road in those years consisted almost entirely of farm trucks carrying the workers from the villages to work, often with no rear lights and very feeble headlights, or farm carts drawn by donkeys or horses carrying loads of maize straw with no lights at all. The surfaced part of the road was so narrow that in order to pass or overtake another vehicle one had to have two wheels on the dirt shoulder. This was the main road from Tulcea to Constanta.

Our rented Volkswagen Beetles were on the whole excellent, especially in coping with the muddy tracks though that is not to say that we did not frequently get stuck and have to dig ourselves out.

The morning we left Bucharest in 1971 I

was told: 'Today we *might* see a red-breasted goose.' Arriving in 'goose country' at 2.30 we found a flock of geese in the air, followed them to a field near a radar station, and in the fading light finally saw them half a mile away in a winter wheatfield – 3,500 geese with small parties still flighting in to join them. Using a telescope we counted 481 red-breasted geese. So, all right, they were a long way off in the dim dusk but there they were, my first wild redbreasts on our first day in the Dobrogea.

White-fronted and red-breasted geese feed, fly, and roost together. The redbreasts seem in a curious way to be dependent on the whitefronts, which are incredibly wild and wary even though they have to a certain extent become used to the scarecrows and irrigation standpipes which are often seen in the fields. Any movement – or a white-tailed eagle in the sky – and they are up in the air, the redbreasts flying close together and the whitefronts more strung out. Inland lakes which form part of the Delta serve as roosts and in some places are screened from the land by tall reeds.

For the next ten days, from dawn till dusk we were never far from geese, yet never close enough to get satisfactory photographs.

On the second day we found 12,000 geese in one not very large wheatfield including about 3,000 redbreasts. Our vigil was disturbed by some sailors in a pony cart who came from the radar station and wanted to see our papers. I think they were delighted to have something new and unexpected like foreign goose-watchers to help them pass the long day, but it didn't help us to keep the geese undisturbed. Later in the week we found 18,000 geese with over 4,000 redbreasts in a huge rolling wheatfield which we had already christened 'The Great Field' next to the main road. This was the biggest flock we had seen so far. The light was poor and the geese were not close so photography was out, but we hatched a plan for the following day.

We had worked out that The Great Field was an unbroken expanse of some 1,300 acres but we had picked our chosen spot the night before, out of sight of the main road. The wheat was green and still untouched and a track lay between it and

A tight bunch of the beautiful little red-breasted geese (above). The number of redbreasts seems to be declining, and the species should be regarded as endangered. It probably totals no more than 10,000

A horse and cart in a Romanian village (top left). Until recently, road traffic consisted almost entirely of farm trucks carrying the villagers to work, and carts loaded with maize straw

Emerging from the Volkswagen hide (left) after a seven-hour goose-watching vigil. The car looked more or less like a haystack with the aid of camouflage netting and straw. An irrigation channel through the Romanian farmland provided good cover for approaching the red-breasted geese – which the party were able to view 'eyeball to eyeball' at a range of about twenty yards

a patch of maize stubble. It was a misty morning as we left Tulcea in the dark but it seemed to be clear above and we hoped the sun would burn it off. We found our muddy track, pulled camouflage netting over our mud-covered little car, gathered some straw with a rake which we had borrowed from the municipal gardens in Tulcea, and added some sheaves of maize straw which were lying about on the track. While we were setting up the last sheaves the geese started to arrive, but by this time the car looked more or less like a haystack. The three of us climbed in and the geese poured over the top of us. Visibility was about 150 yards and the geese were settling out of sight but opposite us. The fog seemed only to extend about ten feet above the ground. We could see the geese overhead against a blue sky – and still they came.

The field of vision from the car was limited but the prospects of the fog clearing seemed good. The shallow layer of mist got shallower and we could see the top of the biggest tumulus in the field (many of these fields have several tumuli in them). And then the geese themselves were in view – first some nearer whitefronts and then the main flock with all its redbreasts. The nearest was feeding downhill towards us although still some 500 yards away. The view was amazing: in this tight swathe on the hillside were 20,000 geese.

I had taken one or two photographs when suddenly they were all up – probably disturbed by an eagle or a rough-legged buzzard, even perhaps in the mist by a hen harrier. We could not see the cause but the effect was one of the most astonishing wild goose spectacles any of us had ever beheld. My husband wrote in his diary: 'They got up in a wave from the left picking up more and more as they went – and were so thick that I particularly noticed a major area of sky, low down over the horizon, which was completely blotted out. It was solid geese without a chink of sky shining through. I have seen this kind of thing with blue geese in Louisiana, but never so dense a blanket – of which a major element was red-breasted geese.'

They swept around and settled again in three places, two of them still quite favorable to us. But then the fog began to come down again and we noticed an ominous change. Looking upwards we could no longer detect blue sky.

The seven-hour vigil in the car continued until 1.30 p.m. At times we could see further than others, at times the geese were flushed, often out of sight in the fog. There were still great numbers in the field but they never came closer than 300 yards and the light was always gloomy.

We breakfasted off hard brown bread, cheese and cherry jam. Butter was a luxury and seldom obtainable even in the hotel. Brandy added to our Turkish coffee in thermoses helped to keep us warm and our spirits up, but the photographic prospects had faded. A horse and buggy finally put paid to it all and we were able to stretch our cramped limbs.

Of the 20,000 geese which had finally got up in the air not less than 6,000 were redbreasts. They often behave like starlings in the air, bunching in tight balls, diving, twisting, and turning – very beautiful to watch. That day has remained one of the most memorable of all our trips to Romania.

In 1977 we arrived in Bucharest on 26 November for a two-week visit, and this time at least the weather was on our side. Out of twelve days in the Delta area we had seven days of good sunshine, two more with sunny intervals, and only one day with a snow blizzard – better weather by far than on our previous expeditions.

There was a noticeable improvement in the roads; some of the side roads into the larger villages had been surfaced, and there was more traffic on the main roads. Most significant of all the changes was the construction of irrigation channels through the farm land. One of these channels provided us on our third day in the area with an opportunity to get really close to the geese. The channel was about fifteen feet deep with some soft mud on the bottom and sloping concrete sides. At that part of the field where the geese were feeding the concrete slabs for the sides had not been put down and were in stacks at intervals along the sides. The channel curved along the contour of the hill. Three of us slithered down the frosty side into the channel and walked along the bottom until we reckoned we were opposite the geese. The sun was behind us and we hoped that by easing ourselves up against one of these piles on the far side, the geese would not detect us in the shadow. The nearest ones were some fifty yards away and they were thickening up all the time. This was what we had been waiting for. The sun was shining full on them and excitement ran high. We must have been there about fifteen minutes, but then alas! – a small party of whitefronts circling overhead saw us and squeaked an alarm.

The geese took off, but they landed again farther on and we moved along the channel bed again. This time we crawled up on the same side as the geese and found ourselves

A flock of white-fronted geese taking off, with some redbreasts among them. To some extent the redbreasts seem to rely on the wary and ever vigilant white-breasted geese, which will fly up into the air at the slightest hint of any movement near the flock

suddenly looking at redbreasts barely twenty yards away through two screens of vegetation – weeds growing each side of the track on the edge of the channel. This was the closest we had ever been.

We had other views of the geese during those two weeks but we were never so close again and no other view of them could compare with those breathtaking minutes when we seemed to be looking at them almost eyeball to eyeball.

The number of red-breasted geese appears to be declining. We have a figure given to us by Russian ornithologists of 25,000 in January 1967. In 1969 there were an estimated 29,300, a peak which occurred in early December. In 1971 the largest flock we saw in a period of ten days and extensive area coverage was 6,000. In 1977 we estimated that over the whole area we may have seen a total of about 40,000 white-fronted geese, 3,500 redbreasts, 1,100 grey-lags and one bean goose. Because the weather was not very cold it is possible that some may have remained in a wheat-growing area just to the north of the Delta in the USSR. But in spite of that the numbers seem to be going down. The red-breasted goose must now be regarded as an endangered species with probably not more than 10,000 individuals left. The Academy of Sciences in Bucharest assures us they are protected in the Dobrogea, but it is doubtful if the law can be enforced. We know there is considerable disturbance from farming activities and the modernization of farming methods. We also know that the geese are shot.

Their breeding grounds in Siberia have suffered disturbance from commercial fishermen and their dogs while the geese are breeding and molting. They have also been affected by the decline in numbers of peregrine falcons, resulting from the use of pesticides, for surprisingly redbreasts like to nest on river cliffs and screes under the protective umbrella of a falcon's eyrie. It appears that peregrines, gyr falcons, and even rough-legged buzzards keep Arctic foxes away, and sometimes as many as eight to ten redbreast pairs would benefit from the 'fighter cover' provided by a pair of hawks. Recently these colonies have fallen to four or less.

The Russians are aware of the problem, and to a certain extent the Romanians too, but we must continue all efforts to safeguard the world population of this extraordinarily beautiful little goose.

DANGEROUS JOURNEY
Janet Coates Barber

The writer Lawrence Durrell, describing the trapping of migratory song birds in Cyprus some years ago, told how:

The bird swarms . . . ripple away from the beaters, pouring along the ground like locusts or pouring from tree to tree, until they suddenly find themselves in the traps which await them. At once the air is full of the anguished fluttering of their wings and their pitiful screaming.

Bird liming – a method used widely on that island – involves a mixture of glue, or tree sap, and honey, which is daubed on small sticks; these are then placed on the branches of shrubs and trees to entrap alighting birds. The birds either die hanging upside down on the twigs, or are removed by the trapper and killed. Liming still continues on a wide scale in Cyprus, and the trapping and shooting of songbirds and millions of other migratory birds takes place on an enormous and undiminishing scale in many European countries.

There are not many wildlife issues about which people in northern Europe feel as strongly, but which have presented so few opportunities for action. Millions of warblers, including whitethroats and blackcaps, flycatchers, and many other species that receive protection in Britain face several million hunters on the continent eagerly awaiting, with guns loaded and traps set, their twice yearly migration to and from Europe and parts of Africa. The interested public in countries which protect their breeding birds are bound to feel frustrated and dismayed if species they have seen nesting in suburban gardens and hedgerows may, because of man's interference, never return or even reach the warm Mediterranean climate. Now, for the first time, efforts are being made to control this massive death toll.

The European national sections of the International Council for Bird Preservation (ICBP) are co-ordinating conservation organizations to form national committees, which are raising money to be spent on projects in the countries where the killing is most severe – for example Italy, France, Malta, and Cyprus and, to a lesser extent, Spain. The British committee, for example, is organizing a fund-raising campaign under the auspices of the ICBP, and the Netherlands committee is also very active. Money raised will be spent on publishing leaflets, posters, and other educational material, the gathering of information, the strengthening of local conservation bodies who seek help, and, in the future, the setting aside of reserves where migrating birds can rest, feed, or winter in safety.

A petition backed by more than eighty organizations representing seven million members has been sent to the European Parliament. The result of this and other representations has been that the EEC Commission has now drafted proposals for the general protection of European birds, which it is hoped will be accepted by the Council of Ministers as soon as possible. An International Convention for the Conservation of Migratory Species of Wild Fauna, embracing migratory animals on a world scale, is in its initial stages, as is a Council of Europe proposal for the conservation of wildlife and natural habitats in Europe.

In 1976 the important basic principle of

A live nightingale caught on a limed stick in Cyprus. Liming is widely practised on that island, and employs a mixture of glue and honey to trap the bird, which then either dies hanging by its wings or is killed by the trapper

48

the Convention was established – that migratory species are a common resource for which all states involved bear responsibility. Governmental initiative, at whatever level and however welcome, is likely to take some time to develop and have impact. It is hoped that the ICBP national committees will be able to act quickly and complement intergovernmental measures.

Views of what 'game' species are vary considerably from one country to another, and laws and the degree of enforcement differ even between provinces or counties in the same country. It may seem strange to some people that migrating waders like redshanks and bar-tailed godwits, and geese, overwintering in Britain can be shot there, or that the French devote so much time to shooting sandpipers, ring ouzels, and golden orioles. Fewer would question the description of pheasant or partridge as 'legitimate game'. We should remember that although widely protected in northern Europe, the annual illegal toll of birds of prey certainly far exceeds that of Malta where there is an appalling legal toll of about 1,500 migrating honey buzzards, kestrels, hobbies, and harriers each year. The turtle dove is not considered game in Britain, but the whole breeding population migrates and 250,000 are shot annually by the Maltese.

When birds provide a source of necessary and irreplaceable food as they did once in most countries – and still do in many – any criticism is more muted. In Britain songbirds were once commonly killed for food, as we learn from the 'four and twenty blackbirds' that produced a sufficiently appetising pie for it to be 'set before a Queen'. Crop damage has also been a reason for controlling voraciously feeding birds.

In spite of the ambivalent ethics and legality of hunting, however, the killing of migratory songbirds and birds of prey is one of the most inexcusable forms of slaughter. Songbirds in no way form an essential part of the national diet of any country; birds of prey are perhaps more threatened than any other bird group; both groups receive increasing protection in countries where they breed; the scale of the twice yearly kill is huge by any standards; and, perhaps most important of all, there has been far too little research in the past on the overall impact of

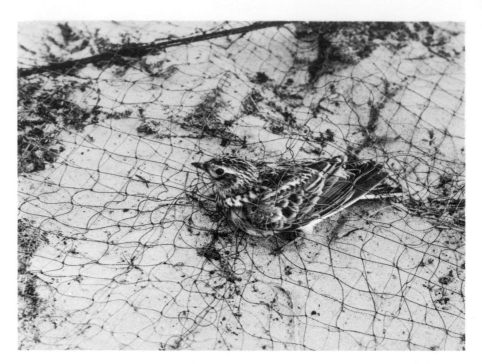

A skylark caught in a trapper's net at Les Landes, in France. It will be squeezed between thumb and forefinger until it is dead. The methods used to kill and trap small migratory songbirds in many European countries may look cruel and unpleasant. But almost worse is the effect this destruction has on the bird populations. At last a concerted effort is being made by birdlovers throughout Europe to control or even end much of this slaughter

hunting pressure on the populations of migrating birds. Combined with other pressures such as loss of breeding habitats, pollution, drought and other capricious environmental factors, the loss of millions of birds out of the breeding populations could have incalculable effects. In Cyprus, as many as seven million birds may be killed annually – and a village in one day could collect about 20,000 birds.

Although the killing of migrating songbirds is characterized by the death of large numbers of a single species, many rare and local species inevitably die as well. Cyprus warblers, pied wheatears, Ruppell's warblers, and scops owls are amongst the scarce birds which are also plucked, lightly boiled, and eaten with the evening aperitif.

Many of the northern breeding populations of songbirds, including the whitethroat, blackcap, willow and garden warblers, whinchat and nightingale, migrate south in autumn and return north in the spring to breed. These and many other species will be brought down by live decoys, whistles or clap nets in south-west France, where a *minimum* of about five million birds are killed annually. Buntings which migrate over the low passes of the Pyrenees to the Mediterranean and Africa, fly through the Armagnac area of France, straight into small traps known as *matoles*. They are then put into a dark cage, fed on millet until they get fat, and killed by smothering or having their heads dunked in brandy. They are cooked in their own fat and eaten whole. In Italy, two million hunters are licensed and a total of well over 150 million birds may well die annually. Species include warblers, finches, larks, and buntings. Birds are either eaten, stuffed for display, bottled, canned as paté, or kept as cage birds.

For the first time ever, a real opportunity now exists to help change public opinion. Practical conservation can then be undertaken in countries which most need it, the people of which are responsible for the safe passage of millions of birds that breed in northern Europe.

CALIFORNIA CONDOR
Faith McNulty

alifornia condors are great black vultures – America's largest birds – that soar on sibilant wings over the mountains and canyons of southern California. Forty years ago some naturalists thought them on the verge of extinction, and yet the huge birds have hung on, surviving an increasing variety of intrusions and assaults.

Now, however, the men officially in charge of condors have concluded that the end is near. A biologist from the US Fish and Wildlife Service has declared that condor reproduction is so low that there is no hope for the species in the wild, and reports that condors do not breed or attempt to nest. The cause of this change in their behavior has not been determined.

Back in 1939 Carl B. Koford of the Museum of Vertebrate Zoology at Berkeley attempted to carry out a census of condors, a far from easy task as condors do not flock like starlings and are highly mobile. By 1941, when his study was complete, he had reached an estimate of a total population of about sixty birds, of which at least fourteen were immature. From this and other evidence Koford concluded that the birds were breeding normally. He warned, however, that the condors were beset by a host of man-made dangers. Hunters were an increasing menace. Loss of roosting, nesting, and feeding habitat also imperilled the birds. Noise and disturbance, from road building, oil drilling, and similar activities threatened to disrupt their nesting and rearing of young.

Koford was disturbed by the use of a variety of poisons in condor range, in view of the danger that condors might eat poisoned carrion. In the 1920s and 1930s thallium sulfate and strychnine were used lavishly in condor range to kill ground squirrels. In 1945 a new poison, Compound 1080, was introduced. The tolerance to this poison of raptorial birds, a group that includes the condor and its cousin, the turkey vulture, was comparatively high, and after some sketchy experiments with buzzards at a Fish and Wildlife Service laboratory, 1080 was officially pronounced 'safe' for condors. But the long-term effect – on young birds, or the fertility of adults – has not been investigated.

Following Koford's study, a Condor Advisory Committee was established, and in 1965 a new report, produced by Alden H. Millar and Ian and Eben McMillan, was published. This catalogued a dismaying variety of dangers pressing in on the condors. Hunters led the list, followed by all sorts of harassment and disturbance, abetted by the indifference of wildlife officials. Croplands in condor range were heavily treated with pesticides. The Forest Service was spraying thousands of acres with herbicides. Poisons to kill predators and rodents were in wide use. Ian McMillan wrote: 'I doubt any region in the world has seen poison used so extensively, so effectively, and with so much ingenuity as the range of the California condor.' Worst of all, the estimate of condor numbers was a total of only forty to forty-two birds. If accurate, this was a startling loss of 30 per cent in twenty years.

One problem which the Advisory Committee has had to face over the years is that the final decision lies with the government agencies having jurisdiction over land and wildlife. These agencies have many interests,

The California condor is America's largest bird, and although it has managed to hold back from the brink of extinction for forty years, ornithologists fear that the end may be in sight for this magnificent creature

some in conflict with condors. Twenty years ago the superintendent of Los Padres National Forest considered the condor a millstone around his neck, interfering with such 'enhancement' projects as roads, fire control, and recreational improvements. Times have changed, but condors remain a potential headache to the California Department of Fish and Game. Hunters and fishermen are the department's prime constituency. Whenever a condor is shot, hunters get bad publicity, but closing condor range to hunters stirs their wrath. Both county and state agencies are involved in long-established and politically popular poisoning programs. Should it be demonstrated that such programs are in fact damaging condors, the result would be a nerve-wracking dilemma for the agencies involved.

Considering the pressures, the advisory committee has won some notable victories for the condors over people and profit. In 1970 the US Department of the Interior put a moratorium on oil and gas leasing in the Sespe condor sanctuary, and the Bureau of Land Management suspended mineral leases within certain other areas, frustrating the plans of the US Gypsum Company to open a huge phosphate mining project. In 1972 the Forest Service closed the public corridors through the sanctuary to firearms, and in 1973 the California Assembly prohibited low-flying aircraft over the sanctuary. Unhappily, the condor population failed to rise in response.

Most unfortunate of all has been a deep division among the ranks of those trying to save the condor, and centering on the debate as to how far the use of pesticides and other poisons has been responsible for their decline. Carl Koford and the McMillans have always pressed for more detailed research into the role of poisons, pesticides and pollution. Fred Sibley, the biologist assigned by the Fish and Wildlife Service to study condor problems; John Borneman, appointed by the National Audubon Society as a full-time condor warden in 1964, and Sanford Wilbur, who took over from Sibley on the Condor Advisory Committee in 1969, have all tended to stress other factors.

In 1972, after three years' work, Wilbur issued a report in which he estimated that

54

The condor is threatened because the rate of reproduction of birds in the wild is very low. There is disagreement over why this should be, but pesticides and other poisons used in agriculture are likely culprits

Condors are really great black vultures. Since the wild birds face such a bleak future, the only hope appears to be a program of captive breeding, followed by subsequent release of the birds in the wild

there were sixty condors – the same figure that Koford had reached in 1941 – but that the reproduction rate was very low, averaging two or less young each season. Few birds were nesting, and Wilbur concluded that this was due mainly to two causes – disturbance of nesting condors and dwindling food supplies.

As a result of these alarming reports, the Californian Condor Recovery Team was set up, under the jurisdiction of the US Fish and Wildlife Service's Office of Endangered Species, and in December 1974 it issued its 'recovery plan'. Of more than sixty proposed steps, virtually all related to protecting condors by lowering the death rate from shooting and other accidents, enhancing reproduction by providing adequate nesting, roosting and food, improving the condors' public relations, and keeping track of their progress. The plan suggested that the 'possibility' of sublethal poisoning should be investigated, but omitted such research from its list of priorities. The success of the recovery plan rested on the premise that the condors were in good health and that it was primarily lack of food that inhibited reproduction. Of 1080 and thallium, Wilbur wrote, 'There may be hazard . . . but no certain losses can be attributed to them.' He also reported that their use on federal land had 'lessened', and claimed that poisoned ground squirrels 'usually die in their burrows.'

Koford and the McMillans strongly disagreed with this. The McMillans had watched many poisonings and found that the number of dead animals above ground was highly variable. Koford urged that while few condors might have died as a result of 1080, no one knows whether poisoned squirrels fed to nestlings affect their survival or their later ability to reproduce. 'Could it be that nestlings fed poisoned meat in the 1950s are today's nonbreeding adults?', he asked. He called, not for the first time, for extensive tests on the effects of poison on turkey vultures, a related species. He also asked if there had been any tests for DDE (a breakdown product of DDT) in condor eggshells.

This last question was brought into prominence when tests on a dead condor picked up by Borneman in November 1974 showed 200 parts per million of DDE in the dry muscle tissue. As usual, there was considerable debate as to the significance of this finding, but in 1975 work began on a study of the thickness of condor eggshells, and a report was completed early in 1977. Wilbur's researchers found that the shells of condor eggs collected between 1964 and 1969 averaged 30 per cent thinner than those of 'normal' eggs collected prior to 1964. The microscope scanning of the later samples showed defects like those in the eggshells of other species of birds affected by DDT. Since then other scientists, in Canada, have tested the same eggshells for DDT and found it – the first direct evidence of its presence in condor eggs.

In the late 1960s brown pelicans were hard-hit by DDT, and it was shown that the thinning of their eggshells was in direct proportion to the amount of DDE in the bird. The breaking point was reached when the shells were about 20 per cent thinner than normal. After DDT was banned in California, the eggshells of pelicans began to improve. This might seem to offer hope that if DDT has affected the condors they too may improve. However, the DDT-affected pelicans continued to nest and lay eggs even though the eggs were not viable. This gives importance to Wilbur's report that the condors' low reproduction is not the result of broken eggs but of a failure to nest at all, suggesting a cause other than, or additional to, DDT.

In early 1976 the Patuxent pesticide laboratory started work on a project to analyse 'residues of environmental pollutants in California condors, their feces and food', but at first Wilbur was only able to send them feathers taken from Topatopa, a female condor in captivity at Los Angeles Zoo since 1967. Thus no analysis of wild condor material took place until late in 1976, when a hunter's bullet provided another condor carcass. The Patuxent laboratory found 105ppm of DDE in fat and 12ppm in the flesh – an amount that it classes as moderate. But these results were undoubtedly modified by the bird's long fast after it was wounded and by its 'clean' diet before its death in captivity.

In 1973, a year before the recovery plan was in its final form, both the National Audubon Society's Roland Clement and Ray Erickson at Patuxent had raised the question of what to do if the plan didn't work. The alternative chosen by the advisory committee was captive breeding, and the proposal for a capture plan was sent to Washington for approval in 1976.

Its premise was that 'because of the low numbers of condors, and the already serious decline in production and in overall quality of habitat,' the recovery plan hadn't helped. The new plan proposed that seven condors should be captured, three the first year, and if all went well, four the second. With Topatopa, the seven condors would, if the sexes were properly assorted, form four pairs. If the birds laid eggs, those eggs, or perhaps chicks, would be taken from them to stimulate additional eggs, as has been done successfully with Andean condors at Patuxent. Eventually captive birds would be released in condor territory.

Techniques to release captive-reared condors have not been developed. The plan relies on the hope that current projects with Andean condors, turkey vultures, peregrine falcons, and whooping cranes will show the way during the five- to ten-year period needed to raise condors for release. Wilbur and Erickson think that condors may be easier to return to the wild than some other species, since they need not learn to kill live prey. The plan summarizes the outlook thus: 'Without the project it is anticipated that the condor population will continue to diminish in size and become extinct. However, there is no guarantee that the project will reverse current trends.'

The need to capture condors was bolstered by a report by Jared Verner, a US Forest Service ecologist, who was asked to appraise the condors' situation and the Forest Service's role in the recovery program. His main conclusion was that unless the condors achieved an output of five or six fledged birds each October, the population might well continue its downward slide to extinction. Verner recommended serious attention to the possibility that toxic substances are inhibiting reproduction and advised a concerted effort to identify their source by means of air sampling, an analysis of the condors' food web, and tests

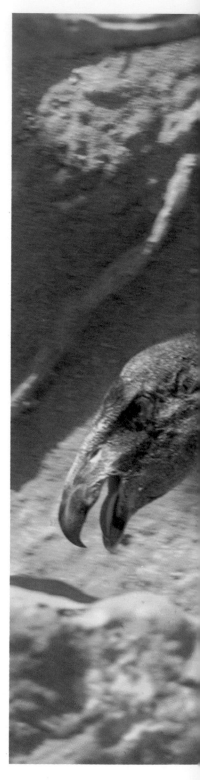

While captive breeding of the California condor appears to represent the great bird's only hope, this is easier said than done. There are many problems, among them how to sex the birds that are captured to ensure that there is a balance of males and females; also, how to release the captive-bred young in such a way that they will breed and increase in the wild

on species that share their diet. He also called attention to the lack of basic data, such as the total number of birds, their ages, sex ratios, frequency of breeding, survival rates, and movement patterns. Wilbur has said that it is not possible to gather this data without capturing and marking a good many birds, and Verner endorsed this procedure.

Carl Koford and Eben McMillan, however, remained unconvinced that the capture plan with its attendant risks to the wild flock was justified on the basis of the information at hand. Koford issued a series of comments and critiques of Wilbur's reports, questioning the evidence on which Wilbur's assessment is based. The first step, wrote Koford, should be a complete and impartial evaluation of the evidence by qualified independent scientists.

In December 1976 Wilbur wrote to Wesley Lanyon, president of the American Ornithologists Union, seconding Koford's request for a review before a propogation program is started and promising his co-operation. Last summer, at its annual meeting in Berkeley, the AOU voted to instruct Lanyon to work with Richard Plunkett of the National Audubon Society towards the formation of an AOU advisory panel on the California condor.

As the new panel set to work in December, it found the accumulation of several decades of unanswered questions awaiting it. The problem of 1080 and condors is an example.

Eben McMillan is still waiting for answers to questions that troubled him back in 1963-4. 'Where are the studies of what chemicals in what amounts are being placed in condor range?' McMillan asks. 'Out here poisoning is a profitable business. One flea carrying bubonic plague can bring down a shower of money. Is that why these studies haven't been done?' He fears that the capture of condors may cover up the need for deeper research into difficult areas.

Wilbur has never given much weight to the question of 1080. He explains that in reviewing condor literature he found only three poison deaths, and these were caused by strychnine. He dismisses the reports by the McMillans implicating 1080 in the deaths of condors as 'purely and poorly

inferential'.

Until recently Wilbur was equally skeptical of the danger from other chemicals, including DDT. It was not until late 1977 that Wilbur arranged to have recent material collected that could be analyzed at Patuxent. Wilbur has explained the two-year delay since the study was first approved at Patuxent by pointing out that it had already been shown – by analysis of shell fragments collected ten years ago and of bodies of dead condors – that the birds had been exposed to DDT. He questioned the value of additional evidence. In April 1977 he wrote, 'The problem, if one exists, is almost certainly (note that I said *almost* certainly) not the result of a specific pesticide operation but of a lot of pesticide in the environment generally. Unless a specific source of contamination is found, we can do nothing more than acknowledge the problem and plan around it as best we can. This is what we are doing now with our captive-propagation program.'

In response to a question on the value of more observation in the field, Wilbur said he saw no purpose in it. 'Watching nesting condors would not give us any information about the rest of the flock. The sick ones are not nesting, so there is nothing to watch.' Asked for his assessment of the condor situation after the 1977 nesting season, Wilbur expressed it in one word – 'terminal'.

Richard Plunkett, however, feels that research is long overdue. 'Because condors are long-lived and pesticide residues accumulate year after year, we should have been expecting this problem all along and looking for evidence of it. Captive breeding should be closely linked to a strong and greatly expanded research program.'

At Patuxent a program of breeding Andean condors as a pilot project for propagating and releasing California condors has progressed far enough to show that condors can be bred in captivity and also that condor breeding may be a long-term affair. Most of the Andean birds were immature when captured, and it took them some time to tolerate captivity. The birds' first successful nesting was seven years after capture. Now all four pairs have bred and produced a total of six young. Like California condors, wild Andeans breed every second year. However, the captives have produced a second egg when the first was taken away and put in an incubator. Erickson describes the project as exceeding his fondest hopes.

Erickson is cautious in blaming DDT for the California condor's decline. He says that other factors, or a combination of them, may be equally significant, and he prefers to withold judgement until there is better evidence. Lucille Stickel, director of the Patuxent research center, is likewise unconvinced that the evidence of DDT so far discovered solves the case. She mentions the possibility of heavy metals, thallium, 1080, and strychnine, as well as chlorinated hydrocarbons. 'The physiology of vultures should be studied. Possibly they can't excrete chemicals or are particularly susceptible to them. Birds circulate air through their bodies. What are soaring condors accumulating from polluted air and at what levels?'

If California condors are bred in captivity, the final hurdle will be finding a way to release the young so that they breed and increase in the wild. Erickson hopes that within seven or eight years there will be two dozen or more captive Andean condors with which to experiment.

The first experiments in releasing captive-bred vultures are beginning this year, directed by Stanley Temple. Temple will experiment with turkey vultures captured in Florida, where they are abundant. Discussing these experiments, Temple recently said, 'The release of condors presents a lot of problems that are not inherent in other species that have been successfully released. The long dependency of young vultures makes it a very complicated situation.'

However, before the capture of California condors is even attempted, a number of matters must be settled: who will direct the operation, how will the birds be caught, where and in what conditions will they be kept? Temporary holding facilities will be needed wherever the traps are set. Also needed is a quick way to determine the sex of the birds that are caught in order to get an equal number of each sex. Hormones in fresh fecal samples can indicate sex, provided the bird is in breeding condition, but this requires trapping condors during the breeding season and risks disrupting breeding. An alternative sexing method involves examination of the chromosomes in the pulp of emerging feathers. Unfortunately this takes several weeks: long detention would add hazards for birds that will later be released because they are of the wrong sex, so short cuts must be developed.

In December 1977 Michael Fry, a specialist in bird physiology, began research at the University of California using a group of captive turkey vultures. The aim is to perfect techniques for sexing condors by analysing steroid hormones in turkey vultures, and in Topatopa, the captive condor at the Los Angeles zoo, and also to identify abnormalities which might affect reproduction. If he is successful it is possible that wild condors may be sexed without capture and their reproductive state diagnosed by collecting droppings as they gather to feed.

The final decision on whether to capture condors lies with the director of the US Fish and Wildlife Service and with the California Department of Fish and Game. The panel of scientists now reviewing the condor problem has no official power, but its recommendations will be extremely persuasive to those responsible for whatever action is taken. The panel's report will shape the next chapter in the history of the condor — the great, black, unbeautiful bird whose soaring flight has been so nearly brought to earth by invisible webs of man's design.

SAVING THE SAND LIZARD
Stephen Bolwell

The dry lowland sandy heath of mid-summer is alive with the passage of a host of small insects, camouflaged by, or hiding beneath the purple flowering heather that is laced with an intricate mesh of spider engineering, revealed only by the early morning dew.

It is something of a surprise to stumble across a relatively large lizard amongst the lazy drone of shimmering color, at first motionless and then scuttling from the path ahead. A bright green giant, jolting the eye from the perspective of the smaller life.

The presence of this unlikely British reptile, the sand lizard, is real enough, although the future of this rare animal is now in question. If one were to make a list of British animals heading for extinction, at the present time the sand lizard would be a likely contender for the top position.

Lowland sandy heath is now one of Britain's most restricted and rapidly disappearing natural environments. As a result, the sand lizard (along with a number of other plant and animal species) is threatened. The southern English county of Dorset contains many of the last strongholds of sandy heath in Britain, considered within the last half century to have been amongst the most representative of their kind in Europe. With a soil too poor to warrant clearance for agricultural purposes, they remained without major disturbance for hundreds of years. That was until fairly recently, when these well drained and easily cleared areas began to be exploited for housing and industrial development. The result has been a rapid, almost random segmentation of the heath, that has left isolated pockets, often too small to withstand further pressure.

Fire on a large heathland is a natural enough hazard. An area is burnt off, and later provides a site for the growth of new heather and eventual recolonization by other plants and animals from the surrounding heath. The new mini-heaths are prone to total destruction by fire. Recolonization is then impossible for anything other than windborne forms. Sand lizard colonies may therefore disappear during the course of a single afternoon. This was the case during the drought summer of 1976 when many large as well as small British heathlands were devastated by fire.

One heath in east Dorset, bordered on three sides by urban development, has escaped fire in recent years. As a result, it has other problems. There is encroachment on one side by young conifer and birch trees, which if uncontrolled will transform the whole site into woodland. And there is a high proportion of dead heather, another legacy of the 1976 summer, that will not support life to anything like the capacity of the healthy plant. Despite the problems, this heath contains a strong, largely undisturbed population of sand lizards – one of the few that still exist, although for how much longer is another question.

On this site, with recent mild winters, the lizards have emerged early in the spring, basking quite openly, their body markings providing ideal camouflage against the heather. The color of the male increases through the spring to an intense green that is worthy of any tropical reptile. At this time of year, the males appear to lay claim to a territory from which encroaching males are chased. Fighting is unusual, and largely

The sand lizard (this one is a female) is possibly the most endangered British animal. It is threatened by the rapid disappearance of lowland sandy heath, its preferred habitat

replaced by an elaborate display, basically a spoof posturing that increases the apparent stature of the body to the opponent, with the aim of discouraging any further action on his part, other than a discreet withdrawal from the immediate vicinity.

Courtship of the female is not a delicate affair. The male grabs the female in his jaws by the flanks or tail. If she is not ready to mate, he is treated to an unceremonious drag through the heather. The rape of such an active partner is impractical, if not impossible. It is not until the female is ready to mate that she remains stationary.

The sand lizard is an egg-laying species, a factor that does not enhance survival on today's trampled heathlands. In midsummer the female selects a site, in fact several sites, since she is rarely satisfied with the first, and digging begins with rapid alternate clockwork strokes of the forelegs, until she arrives at a suitable depth for deposition of her eggs.

The young hatch and tunnel out during August. They begin feeding almost immediately, quartering the heather in a continuous search for small spiders and insects, the food supply so essential if their first precarious winter's hibernation is to be successful.

The sand lizard cannot survive if sandy heathland is to continue to disappear at the present rate, or if the present segmented heath now in suburban areas is to be treated as waste ground suitable only for dumping rubbish. The latest threat is young motorcyclists whose indiscriminate riding is converting some of the remaining heath areas to a barren, desert-like condition.

It is not surprising that two other animals on Britain's Endangered Species list, the smooth snake and the natterjack toad, are also restricted to the same disappearing environment. The law protects these animals from human molestation. However, such a law is totally meaningless if there is no provision for their habitat – which in the course of a single generation has all but disappeared.

For the areas that do remain, conservation would seem a vitally important objective. Unless, like some of the Dorset heaths, they are discovered to be rich in oil . . . in which case rather sophisticated

arguments are needed if developers are to be convinced of the value of the natural wealth that lies above, rather than beneath, the heather.

Fire on heathland (above) has always been a natural hazard, but now that the large heath areas have been fragmented by development, fire can totally destroy an area, without any possibility of its being recolonized by plants and animals from surrounding areas. This female sand lizard (above right) survived a fire, but lost her toes while crossing the smouldering heath to safety. Two male lizards (below right) contest a territory

THREATENED TREES
D. A. Burdekin

The ravages of Dutch elm disease over the past ten years have aroused considerable scientific and public interest in landscape trees. It was estimated that by the end of 1977 about eleven million elms had died out of an original population of twenty-three million in southern Britain. Furthermore, the disease is expected to continue unabated for several more years. No other tree disease has caused such devastation in Britain, and indeed there are only a handful of tree diseases which have caused damage on this scale elsewhere in the world.

A study of these destructive diseases reveals that they have a number of features in common. For example, they have often arisen as a result of the introduction of a foreign pathogen – or causative agent – into a native tree population, or sometimes as a consequence of planting an imported host tree which has proved susceptible to a native pathogen. In those circumstances where the host tree has evolved in the absence of the pathogen, selection pressure for development of disease resistance has also been absent. Such hosts may therefore be particularly susceptible to the disease organism if the two are brought into contact.

On the other hand, many pathogens of trees have evolved broadly in association with their hosts, and host resistance is likely to be relatively well developed: if this were not the case their survival could be severely threatened. Over 600 diseases are listed for Britain alone, and most will fall into this category. A large proportion of these are minor, trivial ailments which often pass unnoticed by the casual observer but some, from time to time, are a cause for concern.

Outbreaks of these diseases may occur when environmental factors such as climate, soil, or management practices are particularly favorable for the development of the disease. These factors may also be important in the development of more serious epidemic diseases – but these have the additional advantage of attacking a more susceptible host.

Examples of both devastating and less serious tree diseases are discussed below in order to illustrate factors influencing the initiation and development of disease outbreaks. Possible implications for the control of tree disease are briefly reviewed in the light of these considerations.

Dutch elm disease is a prime example of a disease which has been introduced from abroad and has had a dramatic impact on the native elm populations of Europe and North America. It was first identified (in Picardy, France) in 1918 and in the following ten years it was found in several other European countries. The first record in England was in 1927 on an elm at a golf course in the county of Hertfordshire. The source of infection for the original outbreak in Europe has never been traced though

No other tree disease has caused as much devastation in Britain as Dutch elm disease, and only a few have caused such damage anywhere in the world. These elms have been killed by the disease, which is actually a fungus carried by a bark beetle. Britain's elms have been reduced by more than half to about 11 million by Dutch elm disease – which, despite its name, may have originated in Asia

several scientists have suggested that the disease was introduced on infected material imported from Asia.

The later history of the disease is better documented. It was first reported in the United States in 1931 and the probable source of infection was traced to a consignment of infected elm wood imported from France. In the mid-1960s a more aggressive strain of the disease, responsible for the current outbreak in Britain, was probably introduced on elm logs imported from Canada.

The suggestion that Dutch elm disease originated in Asia is in part based on evidence that a number of Asiatic elms, such as the Japanese elm and the Siberian elm, show a marked resistance to the disease. Indeed, these and other Asiatic species have been used in both Dutch and American programs for breeding elms resistant to Dutch elm disease. It is believed that the disease may be endemic in Asia and that a relatively stable relationship may have been achieved in which the elms have maintained a considerable resistance to the disease so that both the fungus and its host can survive. However, the disease has not so far been identified in Japan or China (although it has been found in some countries in western Asia) and so this hypothesis must remain mere conjecture.

In the case of chestnut blight, a serious disease of sweet chestnut, the evidence for its introduction into the United States from Asia is more firmly based. The relatively long history of chestnut blight started in 1904 when a forester at the New York Zoological Gardens found some dying chestnuts. A specialist diagnosed the cause of death to be a previously unknown fungus. This fungus attacks and kills the inner bark and occasionally the sapwood of sweet chestnut and is sometimes also found on oak. Cankers are formed on the stem and these may be sunken in appearance if the tissue dies rapidly, or swollen if the attack proceeds more slowly. Two kinds of spores are produced: one is sticky and dispersed by rain, insects, or birds; the other is dispersed by the wind. Either type of spore can infect chestnut stems through bark wounds, and in time a fan-shaped mass develops which may encircle and kill the stem. New coppice shoots may arise below the canker but these in turn may become infected by spores washed down from above.

Although a number of plans were made between 1910 and 1914 to control the disease, including the establishment of a chestnut tree Blight Commission in Pennsylvania in 1913, it had by that time become too widespread for any effective measures to be employed. Over the three decades following the initial discovery of chestnut blight in the United States the disease had almost entirely destroyed the American chestnut through the whole of its natural range.

The source of the original outbreak in New York in 1904 was never traced but in the autumn of 1912 the disease was found in a nursery in North Carolina on chestnut plants imported from Japan. At the same time an American botanist was exploring the forests of northern China. A message was sent requesting him to send back to the US any specimens of diseased chestnut which he found. As a result the presence of chestnut blight in China was confirmed by scientists in Washington, DC. The same botanist later found the disease in Japan.

In 1938 chestnut blight was found in Italy (possibly following introduction from North America) where it caused serious damage to chestnut plantations. It subsequently spread to other countries in southern Europe. Following its initial impact, however, the disease has declined and is no longer the menace it was. Nevertheless, the disease could become serious once more and there are strict plant import regulations to prevent the importation of this disease into Britain.

In 1925 the first breeding program aimed at breeding chestnuts resistant to the disease was started in the United States. In this and later programs various crosses were made between the American chestnut, the Chinese chestnut, and the Japanese chestnut. In this way the qualities of good tannin and nut production from the American chestnut were combined with blight resistance from the Asiatic species (some of which were also good nut producers). The planting of selected varieties of blight-resistant chestnut is now recommended in the United States.

There are several other examples of disease where a similar history of introduc-

Oak blight, or oak wilt (above), is so far found only in the United States. However, strict precautions are taken to prevent its moving to Europe, as it is caused by a fungus similar to that of Dutch elm disease

Diseased elms (right) marked for felling in a London suburb. This is one of the main control methods used to slow down the spread of Dutch elm disease. When undertaken in sufficient time, sanitation felling can be quite successful; another interesting possibility being considered is a form of biological control

tions have been described including white pine blister rust, jarrah dieback, and *Dothistroma* blight. White pine blister rust has a particularly interesting history as it was a disease of little consequence in both Europe and Asia until a susceptible host, *Pinus strobus* (a white pine), was introduced from America into Europe. By 1900, some time after the original introduction, blister rust had become endemic in the large scale European plantings of white pine which had been established by that time. Some time before 1906 the disease was imported into the United States on infected nursery stock and since then has caused immense damage to several important pine species native to North America.

Beech bark disease is caused by a combination of an insect, the beech coccus, and a fungus. It has been present in Europe for at least a century and sporadic losses from the disease have occurred in several European countries during that time. The beech coccus was introduced into North America in about 1890 and since that time beech bark disease has been spreading through natural beech forest areas killing large numbers of trees.

A sporadic disease which has attracted some attention in Britain recently is sooty bark disease of sycamore. This disease is caused by a fungus which probably infects the trees through wounds of various types. Under favorable conditions the fungus invades extensive areas of the woody tissues in which a green, yellow, or brown stain develops. This colour fades if the fungus spreads to and kills the bark. The first outward sign of the disease is a wilting and discoloration of the foliage in part or all of the tree's crown.

Serious outbreaks of sooty bark disease occurred in 1948, 1960, and 1976-7 which were seasons following particularly hot summers, though some reports of the disease were received in intervening years. It appears that spread of the fungus in the wood of living trees is greatest when summer temperatures are high. Additional observations on the geographic distribution of the disease during 1977 have indicated that the disease is limited to those regions where high temperatures were recorded during June, July or August. Control by felling is

not recommended and outbreaks will probably subside without man's intervention – unless, of course, there is a dramatic change in the British climate.

Environmental factors probably play an important role in the development of beech bark disease and sooty bark disease, but other tree diseases are influenced by various management practises. For example, many street trees need to be pruned in order to contain them to an acceptable shape and size. The removal of stems and branches allows decay fungi to enter the tree and these may subsequently develop extensively in woody tissues and render the tree unsafe. There are many examples of such fungi on elm, sycamore, oak, sweet chestnut, and ash. It is standard practise at present to apply pruning wound treatments, often containing bituminous compounds, to prevent entry of decay. However, current research, in both Britain and the United States, indicates that such treatments may not be wholly effective and efforts are being made to find alternative treatments.

The control of devastating diseases such as Dutch elm disease and chestnut blight has clearly proved difficult. There is an incontrovertible case for restricting or prohibiting the international movement of plant material which might carry such diseases. Most countries in the world have now established plant health legislation to

Serious outbreaks of sooty bark disease of sycamore seem to be associated with particularly hot summers. These outbreaks tend, however, to subside naturally without human intervention

Healthy sweet chestnut (top) contrasted with an American chestnut (above), which is dying from chestnut blight. The species was very nearly made extinct by the disease, which has been called the 'greatest botanical catastrophe within the memory of man'

this end. Such legislation must maintain a balance between necessary trade in plants and plant products and the risks of introducing dangerous diseases (or pests).

An example of a disease which must be prevented from entering countries where it is not yet found is oak wilt. This disease is caused by a fungus which is similar in several ways to that causing Dutch elm disease. It has not been recorded in Britain, or indeed anywhere in Europe, and has only been found in the United States. The importation of oak plants from North America is prohibited and imported oak wood must have the bark removed, to eliminate bark beetles which can transmit the disease, and must have a moisture content of less than 20 per cent to eliminate the fungus.

Such measures cannot, however, prevent the spread of oak wilt or other comparable diseases, but every effort is made to ensure that appropriate legislation is introduced and enforced. In addition, contingency plans for dealing with such diseases should they gain a foothold are clearly important.

A range of control measures is practised against established tree diseases, whether native or exotic in origin. These include felling, the application of fungicides, biological control methods and breeding for resistant varieties. The felling and destruction of diseased trees, often referred to as

sanitation felling, is a measure taken to slow down the progress of Dutch elm disease. Provided sanitation programs are started at an early stage in a disease epidemic there is good evidence that the impact of the disease can be markedly reduced.

Fungicides are not widely used for the control of tree diseases because of the high cost and certain practical problems. However, there are exceptions, and the treatment of pruning-wounds to prevent the entry of decay fungi is an attractive technique as it involves application to relatively small areas and is therefore comparatively cheap and straightforward. One interesting possibility in this field, and so far it is no more than this, is the development of a method of biological control, using a biological antagonist to prevent the establishment of decay fungi in pruning-wounds.

A long-term approach to control is the selection and breeding of trees resistant to specific diseases. It is here that a knowledge of the origin of a disease may be important. Thus in the case of chestnut blight it was appreciated that the native populations of American chestnut were likely to be very susceptible to the disease and that resistant chestnuts must be sought from the Far East. Elm breeders have followed a similar course and the latest varieties released to the nursery trade in Holland and the United States include Asiatic species of elm in their parentage. But great care has to be taken in these breeding programs to ensure that other factors such as tree shape and vigor, ability to withstand climatic influences, and resistance to other diseases are all incorporated in the testing procedures.

BOTANICAL TREASURE TROVE
Eric Eckholm

The extermination of a species seldom poses the obvious, immediate threat to human well-being as do certain other kinds of environmental deterioration, such as air pollution and the spread of deserts. Yet, for a wide range of reasons, a decline in the diversity of life forms should be of concern to everyone. Since the impending large-scale loss of species is without precedent and involves the disruption of ecological systems whose complexity is beyond human grasp, no means exist for quantifying the costs. But to be without a price tag is not to be without value. The biological impoverishment of the earth will certainly contribute to the economic, let alone the esthetic, impoverishment of humans. And what is irreplaceable is in some sense priceless.

Probably the most immediate threat to human welfare posed by the loss of biological diversity arises from the shrinkage of the plant gene pools available to agricultural scientists and farmers – a critical aspect of the more general problem. While the global spread of modern agricultural methods and hybrid seeds has brought needed increases in food production, it has in many areas also entailed the substitution of relatively few seed varieties for the wide array of strains traditionally planted. At the same time, forest clearance, grazing, and the spread of cultivation to unused lands may wipe out the wild relatives of domestic crops that still exist in some regions.

Switching to more productive strains is usually necessary and socially desirable. Unaccompanied by adequate seed collection, however, such 'progress' can involve the extinction of unique crop varieties that are closely adapted to the local environment and highly resistant to local pests.

Half a century ago, 80 per cent of the wheat grown in Greece consisted of native breeds; today, more than 95 per cent of the old strains have virtually disappeared, replaced by the products of modern plant science. The spread through the Middle East and Asia of new high-yielding wheat and rice varieties since the mid-1960s has inadvertently caused a drastic shrinkage of the gene pools in such traditional centers of crop diversity as Turkey, Iraq, Iran, Afghanistan, Pakistan, and India.

Further agricultural progress is undermined as the diversity of genes on which plant breeders can draw declines. A locally evolved strain in some remote corner of the earth may hold the genetic key to an important agricultural breakthrough. Thus, in 1973, Purdue University scientists trying to develop high-protein sorghum examined more than 9,000 varieties from all over the world before they discovered in the fields of Ethiopian peasants two obscure strains with the qualities they sought. Who knows what other irreplaceable plant resources have quietly vanished?

Since pests, diseases, production technologies, and agricultural goals all tend to evolve over time, the maintenance of high-yield agriculture depends not only on major breeding breakthroughs but also on the routine development of new crop strains that incorporate needed traits. Yet countless locally evolved varieties, some undoubtedly with properties of huge value, are being obliterated. As British biologist J. G. Hawkes observes, the genetic diversity borne of some 10,000 years of local adaptation of ancient domestic crops such as

Foxglove, the natural source of digitalis, for which many sufferers from heart disease have cause to be grateful. More than 40 per cent of modern drugs originated in nature rather than in the laboratory

wheat, barley, lentils, peas, maize, potatoes, and others 'is now being swept away'. What were once considered to be 'inexhaustible gene pools are now beginning to dry up; indeed, in some cases the diversity for certain crops, such as wheat and barley in southwest Asia, African rice in west tropical Africa, and fruit trees in southwest and southeast Asia, has almost completely disappeared.' Likewise, the wild relatives of many commercial crops are disappearing just as their use in plant breeding is accelerating.

Even as it insidiously reduces the future options of plant breeders, the planting of large areas to genetically uniform crops also involves serious short-term risks. The more genetically homogeneous the fields, the higher their vulnerability to large-scale losses to pests, diseases, and weather abnormalities. The Irish potato famine of the 1840s provides the classic example of the dangers of monoculture; the decimation by corn blight of 15 per cent of the US corn crop in 1970 and repeated insect devastations of Southeast Asian rice crops over the last decade have underscored the continuing folly of reliance on a narrow genetic base in agriculture.

The preservation of diverse crop strains is, in theory, one of the more manageable aspects of biological impoverishment. Huge numbers of seeds can, with proper care, be stored in seed banks and made available to breeders as the need arises. In response to the alarms sounded by Australian plant geneticist Otto H. Frankel and others, a start towards halting the erosion of the earth's crop genetic resources has, in fact, been made in recent years. An International Board for Plant Genetic Resources, with headquarters in Rome and funded by governments and UN agencies, is promoting a variety of regional seed-collection, storage, and documentation schemes. With the quickening of scientific interest in genetic diversity have also come new genetic salvaging efforts by various national governments. While the global problem is far from solved, and germ plasm already lost cannot be retrieved, the outlook for the conservation of varied crop genetic resources is now brighter than it was a decade ago.

Some scientists have proposed the estab-lishment of zones of crop diversity, farming areas within which cultivation of a traditional assortment of crop varieties would be maintained so that their evolution would continue. A potato-diversity preserve, for instance, could be established in the Andean highlands where the potato originated. However desirable such on-farm conservation may be, though, it will be both expensive and socially difficult to implement and can, in any case, involve only a small portion of the extant crop varieties. Hence it cannot be relied upon as the primary means of protecting agriculture's genetic future.

The future of productive forestry, like that of agriculture, is undercut as the genetic resources on which tree breeders and planters can draw vanish. Unlike agriculture, most forestry still depends on trees growing in the wild. As expanding demands for lumber, firewood, and paper press against the shrinking forests, the areas planted to well-selected fast-growing species will have to increase rapidly. Yet land-clearing, timber harvesting, and the spread of genetically homogeneous tree plantations are all contributing to the disappearance of tree varieties of potential value to foresters as they strive to boost forest-land productivity.

One serious constraint on the development of forest industries in the tropics, for example, has been the relative dearth of coniferous species – best suited for most construction and industrial purposes – in the world's lower latitudes. Highland Guatemala is one of the few tropical areas to sport an abundance of conifers, species whose study and dissemination could possibly open the door for lucrative forest industries elsewhere in the tropical world. But in view of the rapid destruction of Guatemala's mountain forests, warns forester Thomas T. Veblen, 'it is likely that the Guatemalan populations of several of these conifers will disappear before their potential as exotic plantation trees is ever tested . . . If the initiation of a program aimed at the preservation of this gene pool is delayed much longer, the options available to future generations for afforesting much of the world's tropical highlands will be tragically reduced.' As with food crops,

Highland Guatemala (above) is blessed with many varieties of tropical conifers, but these mountain forests are being destroyed with great rapidity. The potential value of the conifers as exotic plantation trees may not be established before they are destroyed forever

Deadly nightshade (right) yields a powerful poison – belladonna or atropine – but one which has a beneficial use in medicine: it is used to relieve spasms, or to dilate the pupil of the eye. Atropine is a chemical compound called an alkaloid, and the alkaloids are among the most valuable of all plant-derived compounds

the collection of the seeds of as many tree species and varieties as possible is essential. Given the length of time it takes to grow a tree and test its qualities, however, seed collections cannot provide anywhere near the research benefits that living forests can.

In an age of plastics and moon shots, few people can appreciate the extent to which humans remain dependent on natural products. Although their harvest is seldom recorded in economic statistics, wild plants and animals are essential to the lives of many traditional peoples in Africa, Asia, and Latin America; this consideration alone justifies serious concern about the degradation of natural areas. But in even the most technologically advanced societies, plants and animals serve a variety of crucial industrial, medical, and other purposes. Numerous industrial gums, oils, dyes, and pesticides come from natural sources and many additional uses for wild species are constantly being discovered. The nearly extinct manatee, a large aquatic mammal, provides by virtue of its prodigious appetite a means for clearing irrigation canals choked by the water hyacinths now proliferating in tropical waterways. And in the lowly pokeweed has been found a snail-killing chemical for use in the battle against schistosomiasis, a snail-borne parasitic disease that debilitates more than 200 million people.

Some species of proven economic value are under acute pressure, but perhaps the greatest social costs of species destruction will stem from future opportunities unknowingly lost. Only a small fraction of the earth's plant species have been screened for medically useful ingredients. Nearly all the food humans eat comes from only about twenty crops, but thousands of plants are edible and some will undoubtedly prove useful in meeting human food needs. In a 1975 publication, *Underexploited Plants with Promising Economic Value*, the US National Academy of Sciences drew attention to thirty-six little-known species with tremendous potential utility. It is a statistical certainty that socially significant uses will be discovered for many tropical plants as more are studied.

No one can confidently say that products of comparable significance to rubber (which

following its discovery in South America became one of the world's most important commodities) or quinine (derived from cinchona bark and for the three centuries up to World War I the only effective remedy for malaria) remain to be discovered. But no one can confidently say they don't, either.

Medical researchers' interest in plant-derived or plant-inspired drugs has risen to new heights over the last few decades. The discovery in the middle of this century of a series of 'wonder drugs' from natural sources (some of which had been used for centuries by traditional folk healers) has 'sparked a revolution,' says Harvard botanist Richard Evans Shultes. 'It crystallized the realization that the plant kingdom represents a virtually untapped reservoir of new chemical compounds, many extraordinarily biodynamic, some providing novel bases on which the synthetic chemist may build even more interesting structures.' An analysis of American prescriptions written in 1967 revealed that 25 per cent contained agents derived from higher plants, 12 per cent were derivatives of microbes, and 6 per cent had agents of animal origin. Hence more than 40 per cent of the modern pharmacopoeia originated in nature rather than in chemists' laboratories.

Realizing that, as one observer put it, 'the humblest bacterium can synthesize, in the course of its brief existence, more organic compounds than can all the world's chemists combined,' scientists are stepping up their investigations both of ancient folk medicines and of hitherto unused plants with intriguing chemical properties. The plant kingdom is receiving special attention from cancer researchers who hope to find tumor-inhibiting agents in nature that can provide prototypes or ideas for synthetic anti-cancer chemicals. Tens of thousands of plant species have been screened for this purpose, but the search has really only just begun – and it is being undermined by the extermination of unexamined species.

One plant-derived class of compounds of particular medical value and promise are the alkaloids. These biologically active chemicals include narcotics such as morphine (found in opium) and nicotine; hallucinogens such as LSD and mescaline; poisons such as that in Socrates' hemlock

Millet, or sorghum, photographed in Ethiopia. It is important to maintain diverse strains of wild crop plants as a gene pool for the future. As it happens, in 1973 American scientists trying to develop high-protein sorghum examined 9,000 strains from around the world before they found what they wanted growing wild in the fields of Ethiopian peasants

brew; and a host of medicines used as painkillers, anti-malarials, cardiac and respiratory stimulants, blood-pressure boosters, pupil-dilators, muscle-relaxants, local anesthetics, tumor-inhibitors, and anti-leukemic drugs. Once extracted from plants, many alkaloids have served as models for synthesis by chemists; some, however, are still obtained solely from natural sources. A tropical periwinkle plant, for example, provides a chemical used to fight leukemia; the plant is becoming rare in some areas because its high commercial value has prompted over-collection. Curare, a muscle-relaxant widely used by anesthetists in the operating room, is distilled from vines in Upper Amazonian jungles by Indians who have long poisoned their arrow tips and blowgun darts with the concentrated extract. Curare is now in short supply, perhaps – buyers theorize – because people have begun harvesting immature vines or perhaps because the Indians skilled at locating and processing the vines are themselves becoming scarce.

Only about 40 per cent of the 4,350 alkaloids known as of 1970 had been chemically analyzed at that time. More significant, only a small proportion of the world's plants have yet been screened for alkaloid contents. Alkaloid-bearing plants appear twice as frequently in the tropics as in the temperate zones, so major losses of potentially valuable compounds are inevitable as tropical habitat destruction spreads.

The extermination of a unique, unstudied organism or ecosystem involves an irreversible loss to science. Basic knowledge about living systems and ecological relationships, of which a great deal remains to be gleaned, is no mere academic concern; it underlies our understanding of how the world works and what our place in it is. Lost scientific opportunities, like lost economic opportunities, are by nature incalculable but they are nonetheless real. We cannot know how long our understanding of evolution would have been set back, for instance, had the unique fauna of the Galapagos Islands been destroyed before young Charles Darwin, about to piece the mosaic together under the visual stimulation of the isolated Galapagos life forms, visited the islands on HMS *Beagle* in 1835.

Beyond particular economic or scientific losses caused by the destruction of particular species lies a more basic threat: the disruption of ecosystems on which human well-being depends. No matter how sophisticated modern technologies may seem, human livelihoods are ultimately grounded in biological processes, enmeshed in ecological webs so intricate that the consequences of destabilization cannot often be foreseen. Crushed by the march of civilization, one species is likely to take others with it, and the ecological repercussions and rearrangements that follow may well endanger people. One common result of ecosystem degradation, for example, is an increase in the prevalence of small, hardy, fast-reproducing plants and animals of the sorts usually considered pests. The consequences of an adverse change in an ecosystem, such as the over-running of crops by pests or the sudden spread of a disease, may easily be perceived as matters of chance when in fact they are the direct results of human actions.

No one could claim that all existing species are ecologically essential to the viability of human culture. But scientists cannot yet say where the critical thresholds lie, at what level of species extermination the web of life will be seriously disrupted. Identifying and protecting those species whose ecological functions are especially important to human society are crucial tasks facing both scientists and governments. In the meantime, prudence dictates that existing organisms should be given the benefit of the doubt as far as possible.

Harvesting potatoes near Chinchero, Peru (above). The potato originated in the Andean highlands and it is suggested that a 'potato-diversity reserve' should be established there as a kind of potato gene pool

The opium poppy (right) – a
plant of great medical
importance, but one with a
tragic reputation

DESERT WILDLIFE
John Cloudesley-Thompson

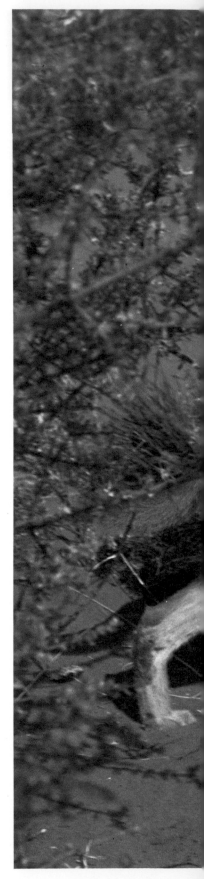

The caracal, photographed here in the Kalahari, is a species of lynx, with typically tufted ears and bearded cheeks. It occurs throughout the African continent and in south-west Asia and like all lynxes is blessed with a savage temperament

Deserts cover about one third of the land surface of our small planet. Nearly two thirds of the countries of the world face 'desertification' problems – the spreading of deserts. The Sahara provides the most dramatic example of this process. This desert is growing at a rate of around three million acres a year, which means that every year Africans lose an area equivalent to Jamaica or the state of Connecticut; every decade the Sahara gains the equivalent of Czechoslovakia or the state of New York. And the growth of the Sahara represents only one fifth of the world's annual losses to desertification.

It is seldom a question of huge sand dunes covering an oasis. The desert moves forward gradually and patchily, wherever overgrazing or unwise cultivation destroys the surface vegetation and lets soil turn into shifting sand. Overgrazing, overcultivation, and deforestation (to provide domestic fuel) are the main causes of desertification in the drylands that fringe the Sahara. And these problems in turn are largely caused by expanding human populations.

In some places the process is irreversible – vegetation has still not healed the tank tracks of the World War II battle of Tobruk – but there is evidence that in many places the deserts can be thrown back. Led by the United Nations, programs are being mounted to re-green the desert lands. While desertification is usually seen as a human problem (some 600 million people live in the shadow of the world's deserts), these arid regions are surprisingly rich in wildlife, as the following account shows.

Mammals

Desert mammals have certain features in common with the mammals of open savanna, steppes, tundra, and high plateaux. In each of these environments the dominant forms tend to be either large, speedy herbivores and the carnivores that prey on them, or subterranean rodents with social habits. The modification of the limbs for the purpose of running and leaping or of digging is often similar in unrelated species from different parts of the world.

There are large numbers of rodents inhabiting different desert regions of the world. Except for the spring-hares of East and South Africa they tend to be about the size of small rats with short front legs and long hind legs adapted for jumping. The tail is long, with a tuft of hairs at the end. Examples include gerbils, jerboas, and kangaroo-rats. Since they avoid the midday heat by burrowing, their problems are concerned with water shortage rather than with thermal stress, and some can even exist on a diet of dry seeds without any drinking water at all. Others, such as the North African sand-rat, feed on salty succulent plants.

The larger mammals of the Old World deserts include antelopes, gazelles, and wild asses. In the arid regions of North America their place is taken by the mule-deer and the pronghorn, formerly very common in the prairies but now extremely rare. The larger herbivores of the Australian deserts are kangaroos and wallabies, whose young are born in an early stage of development and are carried in the mother's pouch until they are old enough to fend for themselves.

None of these animals is able to escape the rigors of the desert climate by burrowing, but all of them have low water requirements and their mobility enables them to travel long distances to obtain drinking water when required. The addax and oryx antelopes usually obtain sufficient moisture from the green plants and acacia leaves on which they browse, while the same is true of the dorcas gazelle over much of its range. Unlike cattle, these herbivores feed mainly at night, when the leaves of trees and grasses contain the maximum amount of liquid. This is one of the secrets of their success in the desert. In common with other animals of steppe and desert, where concealment is scarce and sources of water infrequent, the small saiga antelope of western Asia is also fleet of foot and can cover long distances.

Oryx, whose numbers have been greatly reduced in recent years by hunting, are formidable creatures when angered. Charging the foe with head down, they thrust with their long, sharp horns and emit a curious vocal challenge through their nostrils. The gentle addax, on the other hand, is smaller. Lacking the stamina and speed of the oryx, it is even more independent of moisture, and occurs in very arid desert where few enemies except man can reach it.

The single-humped dromedary or Arabian camel is widespread throughout the Middle East, India, and North Africa: it is known only as a domesticated species. However, the heavily-built two-humped bactrian camel of central Asia still occurs wild in the Gobi Desert. Its long dark hair and short legs are adaptations to the cold winters that it experiences. Both species are economical in the use of liquid, and like asses can safely withstand a degree of desiccation that would be lethal in other mammals. The hump does not store water, but acts as a reserve of food that is drawn upon during the dry season when vegetation is scarce. Only after their body temperature has risen considerably do camels begin to sweat. They tend to store heat during the day and lose the excess at night, thus economizing on the use of water for evaporative cooling of the body. This is a characteristic of most, if not all, desert herbivores.

Desert carnivores tend to be rather small. They include jackals, hyenas, coyotes, wild cats, lynxes, badgers, skunks, pumas, and the almost extinct thylacine or Tasmanian wolf. Until they were exterminated by hunting, lions and cheetahs occurred throughout much of the Sahara. Such animals are able to fulfil most of their requirements for water from the blood and body fluids of their prey.

During the last century the mammal populations of the world's deserts have been considerably impoverished by hunting and wanton slaughter – not so much by the nomads who hunt for food as by sportsmen and soldiers who kill merely for the excitement.

Birds

Compared with small mammals, most desert birds are at a distinct disadvantage because, unable to burrow, they cannot escape from the midday summer heat. Consequently, most species have to live within range of fresh water: elsewhere, they are scarce in comparison with reptiles and mammals. A dramatic example is afforded by sandgrouse, which are distantly related to pigeons. As the sun rises, great flocks of these birds, constantly calling to one another, fly many miles to water. They feed on the seeds of desert grasses.

Sandgrouse nest far away from lakes and rivers, but have developed an extraordinary method of watering their young. The male bird rubs his breast on the ground before drinking, so that the feathers are awry and easily saturated. When he flies back to the nest, the young pass the wet feathers through their beaks and keep changing place until the supply of moisture has been exhausted. The habit of wetting the breast feathers while drinking also serves to cool the unhatched eggs. Other species have to nest in holes, caves, crevices, and under boulders, because the eggs are rapidly sterilized if exposed to the heat of the sun. Pratincoles stand over their developing eggs, thus shading them, while elf owls, screech owls, sparrowhawks and flycatchers in America are dependent upon holes in saguaro cactus, hollowed out by two species of woodpeckers.

Large predatory birds such as eagles,

A cheetah in the Kalahari Desert. It is able to fulfil most of its water requirement from the blood and body fluids of its prey, such as antelopes and other ungulates

(Over page) Ostriches are the largest desert birds, and they can neither fly nor shelter from the heat. But they keep reasonably cool thanks to the shading provided by their feathers and their naked neck, legs, and underparts. Like the camel, the ostrich can endure considerable dehydration without ill effects

vultures, and lammergeiers, spend the day soaring in the cool air high above the desert sand. These birds obtain moisture from the blood of their prey, as do insectivorous birds, but the dry diet of seed-eaters, on the other hand, provides them very little water. They spend the day sheltering in small bushes, or in the shade of rocks. Owls and nightjars are better off, because they secrete themselves down holes and crevices in the ground. The largest bird of all – the ostrich – can neither fly nor shelter from the heat. Since its back and sides are shaded by feathers, however, while the neck, legs, and underparts are almost naked, it manages to keep reasonably cool. Ostriches, like camels, can endure considerable dehydration without ill effects, and allow their body temperatures to become quite high before they begin to pant.

Birds do not possess sweat glands, and when their body temperature increases they can only obtain relief by panting. Although ostriches must drink from time to time, or eat succulent food, they have evolved nasal salt-excreting glands which enable them to live off even quite saline water. The American mourning dove can also endure increased body temperature and extensive dehydration before it begins to pant. This, coupled with the ability to fly considerable

distances, enables it to meet the demands of desert life. Unlike most birds of similar size, the mourning dove is not confined to the vicinity of water.

Like all deserts animals, the birds of arid environments are opportunists. Many carnivorous species feed chiefly on reptiles. The golden eagles and lanner falcons of the Sahara, for example, live to a large extent on spiny-tailed lizards; the African secretary bird and the American road-runner specialize on a diet of snakes; while desert shrikes impale lizards on the sharp thorns of acacia trees.

Many desert birds show concealing coloration that matches the color of the soil where they live. Among familiar examples are desert larks, nightjars, and poorwills, whose cryptic plumage makes them very hard to distinguish when they are not moving. Black plumage is frequently seen among desert birds, including wheatears and ravens. Although there is some dispute as to their function, black feathers certainly render their possessors conspicuous. This may have a social function or serve as a warning in the case of formidable or distasteful species. The same phenomenon is apparent among other animal groups.

The bird fauna of the desert is a restricted one and, because of their vulnerability to

A large predatory bird such as the white-backed vulture (left) obtains moisture from the blood of its prey, and keeps cool by soaring high above the desert sand

A screech owl (right) looks out of its nest hole in a saguaro cactus in Arizona. It depends on woodpeckers to make the holes in which it shelters from the desert heat

the hostile environment, desert birds are in especial need of protection.

Reptiles

Of all animals, reptiles are in many ways the best adapted to life in arid places. Their thick, dry skins are resistant to evaporation; waste products are excreted as a pulpy, semi-solid mass, and their comparatively small size and often elongated shape enable them easily to burrow or seek shelter in rock crevices and naturally occurring holes in the ground. Most of them are carnivorous and obtain from their food all the moisture they require.

Lizards of the dunes either have limbs fringed with elongated scales so that they can run across the surface of loose sand, or else they are adapted for 'swimming' in it. The nose is pointed or shaped like a shovel with the small nostrils directed upwards instead of forwards so that sand does not enter them. The eyes, too, are often protected by the lower lids which may be enlarged and transparent so that their owners can see through them. The ear opening is either small and protected by a fringe of scales, or even abolished in some cases.

Side-winding, as exhibited by the American desert rattle-snake and the horned vipers of the Great Palaearctic desert, enables these snakes to progress by lateral loops and to move obliquely. In this way the proportion of the body surface that is in contact with the hot soil is reduced, and the prey can be approached in an indirect manner that does not alert it until too late.

Like small mammals, many desert reptiles avoid the daytime heat by adopting nocturnal habits. Most of them, however, seem to emerge from their retreats at dawn and dusk, retiring to the shelter of their burrows as the sun rises higher in the sky. In this way, the temperature of the body is maintained at a uniform level and lethal extremes are avoided. Perhaps the most imposing of desert lizards is the African monitor which may reach a length of nearly six feet. It is a speedy and rapacious creature, and will eat any other animal that it is strong enough to overcome.

Although much less common than lizards, snakes also comprise an important element of the desert fauna. Desert snakes have a lower tolerance of high temperatures than have lizards and tortoises. They include the secretive, burrowing worm-snakes and a number of other harmless species, as well as pythons, some back-fanged snakes, vipers, rattlesnakes, and cobras. Harmless snakes greatly outnumber poisonous ones.

The 'asp' with which Cleopatra ended her life must have been either a horned viper or the Egyptian cobra, which is widely dispersed throughout Africa. The name 'asp' has been applied to both of these, but in view of the rapidity with which Cleopatra is said to have died, the cobra seems to be the more likely candidate. It is a swift, irritable creature that strikes with loud hisses, quickly killing its prey with a lethal nerve poison that causes paralysis. The venoms of the vipers usually contain an ingredient that causes clotting of the blood and operates much more slowly than cobra venom.

Desert tortoises lead a more leisurely life. They rise late, go to sleep early, and take a long siesta in their burrows during the heat of the day. The large African grooved tortoise, for instance, digs a deep burrow with its powerful front legs. When overheated, tortoises produce copious saliva that cools the head, neck, and front legs by its evaporation. At the same time, the rear end of the body is cooled by the evaporation of urine which is rubbed on to the hind legs and tail.

Biologists have been puzzled by the large size of the bladder of land tortoises, because it does not seem to act as a reservoir and water cannot be reabsorbed from it. We now know, however, that it is used for cooling the body in an emergency. Urine is also used as a defense against enemies, such as foxes or coyotes. Before and after laying its eggs, the American gopher tortoise wets the sand around the nesting site. This facilitates digging, and prevents enemies from smelling the eggs and eating them. Tortoise urine has a strong and unpleasant odor, especially when it is stale.

Many species of reptiles are highly specialized for desert life. Although most of the smaller forms are probably not endangered, many tortoises are nevertheless becoming scarce through exploitation as pets, and the larger snakes and lizards suffer from being hunted for their skins. It is harder for them to escape notice in the desert than it would be in a more densely vegetated environment.

Fishes and Amphibians

Many deserts contain aquatic habitats – streams, springs, swamps, lakes, and oasis

Gould's sand goanna (above) is found in Australia. The reptiles are amongst the best adapted animals for life in the desert. Their skins are resistant to evaporation, they excrete very little liquid, and they are carnivorous and obtain all the moisture they need from their food

Snakes, like this viper (left), are an important element of the desert fauna, but are less well able to tolerate high temperatures than lizards and tortoises. However, like the larger lizards, some of them are threatened through being hunted for their skins

Several species of pupfish (bottom left) live in isolated underground pools in the Nevada-California desert, especially around Death Valley. Most of them are endangered because pumping for irrigation has lowered the water table

pools – that form the homes of unusual fishes and amphibians. Because of their location, such environments frequently display great variability. Desert rivers, for instance, are often subject to long periods of reduced flow, and are then scoured by major floods. Smaller watercourses may be reduced to a series of isolated pools and often dry up completely. At other times, flash floods change clear, static water into muddy torrents within a matter of seconds. During periods of drought, too, water temperatures may exceed 40°C, and salinity is greatly increased by evaporation. All these factors create problems for aquatic animals.

Despite their impressive violence, flash floods seldom annihilate aquatic animals, but fishes swept downstream frequently perish. This occurs on the Namib and Kalahari deserts of southern Africa when rare flows of water in ancient river beds carry fishes to their doom.

Increased turbidity also imposes severe problems for fishes, which tend to avoid it whenever possible. Some species, however, have acquired various adaptations – such as the development of barbels and leathery skins which resist abrasion, and the evolution of special surfaces within the eye for the concentration of light.

During the seasons of drought in the deserts of the south-western United States, several native fishes (such as longfin dace, gila topminnows, and desert pupfish) are able to survive for a while beneath saturated mats of algae and detritus. Numerous groups of fishes throughout the deserts of the world have species that are adapted for survival in foul and turbid waters, and which can live for months after the water has dried up completely. In some of these air-breathing fishes, accessory respiratory surfaces have evolved within the mouth and digestive tract, while the lungfishes have gas bladders which function like the lungs of higher vertebrates. Such fishes survive in times of drought by burrowing into the mud or moist soil before it has dried out completely.

Many desert fishes can withstand unusually high temperatures, but conditions are sometimes deceptive. Large differences exist in the density of water at differing temperatures so that it is stratified into layers, some of which are very much cooler than the main mass of water, and desert fishes seek out these cooler 'microhabitats'.

In general, frogs and toads are the only amphibians found in extreme deserts, but a species of newt is known to occur in the arid regions of the eastern Mediterranean while semi-permanent pools in the south-west of North America are inhabited by large populations of salamanders. Many of these desert amphibians pass the dry seasons in deep burrows. Some respond to dehydration by decreasing the rate of urinary loss. For most kinds, however, survival depends upon the avoidance of excessive heat and drought. Also, when rain does fall, it is remarkable how quickly eggs are laid and the young hatch. It is of vital importance that metamorphosis into the air-breathing adult form should take place before the desert rain pool dries up.

Although desert fishes and amphibians have become adapted to an inconstant and often unfavorable environment, they are nevertheless extremely vulnerable to human influence. Flash floods do not normally destroy entire populations but, when a dam burst in India, a flood was produced that is said to have destroyed the entire fish fauna downstream. Seasonal rivers are easily polluted, except during the rainy season. The introduction of exotic species, too, has, on occasion, led to the elimination of native desert fishes. The introduction of the water hyacinth into the Nile and its tributaries was followed by reproduction so rapid that the entire ecological balance of the river was upset, and some species of fishes suffered considerable losses.

THE BIRDS OF BHARATPUR
Michael Freeman

Painted storks nesting in an acacia tree – at the Bharatpur sanctuary. It is today one of the world's best known bird reserves, which has an ironic twist: in the past shooting birds was more important than preserving them, as the record (below) shows

Towards the middle of September the first breath of cold arctic air begins to touch the north of Siberia. In the seemingly endless and impenetrable marshes along the meandering Ob River, the scattered families of Siberian cranes start leaving their nests for the winter migration south. From the low-lying tundras, dotted with lakes and stunted trees, these remnants of one of the world's rarest and most elusive bird species make their way slowly southwards, over a route that is still unknown. Occasionally the cranes are seen passing over the Turgai region of Kazakhstan, but for the rest it is a matter of conjecture, particularly the point at which they cross the western Himalayas.

Nevertheless, sometime in November, they appear over the southern foothills of the Himalayas; continuing south across the plain of the Indus and Ganges, the small flocks pass by Lahore and Amritsar. As they pass Delhi the end of the journey draws close, for their final destination is a mere eleven square miles of flooded acacia forest, situated midway between Agra and Jaipur. Here, near the small town of Bharatpur, are the only known winter quarters of the Siberian crane.

As the cranes circle the tree-dotted lakes, their sonorous trumpeting mixes with another sound – the cacophony of countless thousands of nesting waterbirds already in residence, for this small island of trees and lakes in the most densely populated part of agricultural India is one of the world's most renowned wildlife reserves.

The Keoladeo Ghana bird sanctuary at Bharatpur (despite the recent re-naming, it is still universally known simply as Bharatpur) is without any doubt the finest in India.

DATE	ON THE OCCASION OF THE VISIT OF	BAG	GUNS
1902 1ST DEC	1ST SHOOT H E VICEROY LORD CURZON H.E. C-IN-C. LORD KITCHENER	540	17
1903 9TH FEB	2ND SHOOT H.R.H. THE DUKE OF CANNAUGHT	780	19
1903 14TH DEC	1ST SHOOT H.E. VICEROY LORD CURZON	2049	45
1907 15TH NOV	1ST SHOOT HON'BLE MR E. COLVIN A.G.G.	1750	32
1908 30TH NOV	1ST SHOOT HON'BLE COL. PINNEY A.G.G.	2141	33
1908 12TH NOV	2ND SHOOT	1085	27
1909 27TH NOV	1ST SHOOT HON'BLE MR E. COLVIN A.G.G.	3297	48
1909 24TH DEC	2ND SHOOT	504	20
1910 4TH JAN	3RD SHOOT	664	24
1910 1ST DEC	1ST SHOOT H.H. MAHARAJA BIKANER	2758	51
1910 31ST DEC	2ND SHOOT H.I.H. THE CROWN PRINCE OF GERMANY	1379	49
1911 13TH FEB	3RD SHOOT H.H. MAHARAJ RANA OF DHOLPUR	1712	42
1911 8TH NOV	H.H. MAHARAJA BIKANER H.H. MAHARAJ RANA OF DHOLPUR	1285	48
1911 30TH DEC	2ND SHOOT H.H. MAHARAJA'S 1ST SHOOT	1022	29
1912 20TH JAN	3RD SHOOT H.H. MAHARAJA KISHENGARH	1439	41
1912 15TH FEB	4TH SHOOT HON'BLE MR. R.E. HOLLAND	1317	27

During the summer months, from July to October, enormous numbers of indigenous waterbirds gather to breed and nest. Painted storks, open-billed storks, egrets, white ibises, darters, cormorants and many other species begin their nesting shortly after the south-west monsoon, crowding into mixed colonies around the marsh. By November the breeding is coming to an end, with several broods raised, and the colonies are joined by the first of the migratory birds from the north, including the Siberian cranes, ducks, geese, sandpipers, and plovers.

The Birds of Bharatpur

Bharatpur's 7,000 acres of open acacia forest lie in a shallow depression which the monsoon rains run into a shallow lake. The reserve's natural location makes it an ideal site for waterbirds, but if it had not been for its particular historical circumstances, the increasingly urgent pressure on land in these valuable agricultural areas of the Ganges plain would have squeezed it out of existence long ago.

It is ironic that one of the world's most magnificent bird sanctuaries should have been created as a direct result of the Indian nobility's passion for slaughtering wildlife on a regal scale. Created by the Maharajah of Bharatpur as his personal duck-shooting preserve, Bharatpur set some impressive record bags. An engraved marble record still stands near a small temple in the heart of the reserve, celebrating the important shoots at which the Maharajah entertained members of the British Raj. Both Lord Curzon and Lord Kitchener were guests at the first recorded event, on 1 December 1902, when, with seventeen guns, 540 ducks were bagged. Curzon's party improved on this the following winter with a bag of 2,049, but the record was set one day in 1938 when 4,273 birds were shot, with Lord Linlithgow in attendance.

These excesses are no longer indulged in, and the Indian Government has declared Bharatpur a reserve, officially since 1956 but enforced only since 1972. The legacy of these duck-shooting days is the system of artificial flooding that attracted not only the ducks but numerous other species of water-birds. The sanctuary is criss-crossed with raised dykes, or 'bunds', each carrying a footpath, most of them lined with acacias. The dykes control the water level in the shallow lakes they enclose, holding the water of the monsoon rains through the winter and following summer. Around the margins of the sanctuary the slightly higher land carries a rather denser dry forest, and here herds of blackbuck, nilgai, and chital add to the variety of Bharatpur's fauna.

Perhaps the most spectacular first impression is obtained on a visit to the central lake in a flat-bottomed boat at sunset. Late on a December day I left with a guide, poling the boat through the reeds. A large egret stood poised and motionless to our left, staring intently into the shallow water, while in the dead branches of a waterlogged tree, a crested serpent eagle turned its head slowly, scanning the marsh. Ahead of us, a sound that began as a low, indefinable murmuring became louder and more distinct as we pushed through the beds of lilies towards the centre of the lake. From the direction of the noise, a small flock of white ibises flew towards us, arcing sharply away as they saw the boat.

After a while I could see that the clump of partly-submerged acacias ahead was alive with movement, and the noise was becoming overpowering. Every single tree was covered with the open, untidy nests of storks, spoonbills, ibises, and cormorants, its trunk and branches white with droppings. Within a few minutes we were amongst the trees, and as we steered between them, the raucous calls were almost deafening. In the continual flurry of landings, take-offs, and squabbling for perches, there seemed to be no time for alarm at our sudden appearance.

This noisy anarchy stretched over several acres of packed heronries. Local differences soon became apparent, with different assemblies of species in different parts of the lake. The painted stork stronghold was probably the noisiest, and certainly the largest, the ungainly young swaying and flapping on the branches. A little beyond, spoonbills predominated, and farther still a few trees were occupied mainly by white ibises. A crash on one side startled us, and from a nearly-submerged dyke two sambar, disturbed from their grazing, leaped out into the lake, kicking up sprays of water.

As the sun set, we came to the far edge of the central colonies. Looking out over half a mile of open marsh, we could see flocks of sarus cranes stepping through the reeds with their precise leaning gait. Their occasional trumpeting reached far out across the water. Beyond them, in the distance, were more colonies, too far away for us to identify individual birds.

The following dawn I set out by myself to walk along the bunds that enclose the lakes. The previous evening had been breathtaking, rather like being plunged suddenly into a busy street market, but I also wanted to pay a more leisurely visit to some of the colonies. In particular, of course, I wanted to see the

The Siberian crane is the most notable winter visitor to Bharatpur, but the reserve's 7,000 acres is an ideal site for thousands of water-loving birds, both resident and migratory

Bharatpur also has an interesting and respectable complement of mammals: these chital or spotted deer come out to feed in the late afternoon

90

beautiful and spectacular Siberian cranes. Their main area was a secluded and practically inaccessible part of the marsh, but several isolated families were known to feed close to one of the paths.

The beauty of a winter sunrise on the Indian plains is hard to describe; there is an elusive quality about the softness of the light and the mist rising through the trees. In the distance, the sound of a brass cowbell and the occasional calls of a cowherd from one of the nearby villages carry through the still air. Among the trees at the side of the road a solitary black-necked stork that had been feeding in a small pond stepped nervously away from the sound of my footsteps, and finally took flight, flapping quietly towards the lake. The forest soon opened out to reveal the marshes, and I turned on to one of the dykes that crossed it.

Moving quietly along the path, there was little danger of disturbing the hundreds of geese and ducks that filled the water on either side of the dyke. On branches hanging

An Indian darter dries its wings after a fishing spell.
Conveniently located between Jaipur and Agra, the sanctuary shows off its sights to thousands of tourists every year – and teaches them what conservation means in practise

over the water's edge a few Indian darters aired their wings to dry, but in reality, this part of the sanctuary, to the south of the main heronries, is the preserve of the migrants. They arrive at Bharatpur during November and December, from northern Asia as far as Russia, and even from northern Europe. Some, such as the gray pelican, migrate here from within India itself. By the end of February they have practically all returned home to the north.

As I walked along the dyke, a flock of bar-headed geese wheeled overhead. Inadvertently, I disturbed a fish eagle perched in one of the trees by the side of the path, and as it flew slowly away across the lake, large flocks of Brahminy ducks and teals lifted noisily from the water. Finally, near the end of the dyke, I found my Siberian cranes. Two pairs, one of them with its young, stalked gracefully through the rushes. Only a little smaller than the indigenous sarus crane, their brilliant white plumage makes them conspicuous. Each pair stayed close together during their feeding, occasionally spreading their black-tipped wings and just once dipping their heads alternately and trumpeting their distinctive unison call. I could well imagine from these short displays how magnificent the courtship dance must be, in the late spring on the banks of the Ob River.

Bharatpur has the additional bonus of a quite respectable variety of mammal life, mainly concentrated in the slightly higher areas of dry forest around the margins of the sanctuary. The most prominent are the herds of chital or spotted deer; a census undertaken in 1973 recorded 310. There are also about thirty sambar, while antelopes are represented by over 200 nilgai, or blue bull, and a few black-buck. Wild boar are common, and there is even a pair of hyenas that can be heard chattering loudly some nights near the rest house.

Observing these mammals obviously requires rather more diligence than for the wildfowl, but even the casual visitor is guaranteed a view of some chital and wild boar ever since the sanctuary staff instituted evening feeding on a small rise overlooked by the rest house. In fact, facilities for visiting are on the whole excellent. Accommodation in many of India's wildlife reserves has

traditionally been a bit uncertain, and in the height of the tourist season many are booked up long in advance. In the case of Bharatpur, however, the government has taken an active step in catering for tourists, without much interference with the sanctuary's function as a reserve. As well as the long-established Santi-Kutir rest house, which doubles as headquarters for the sanctuary staff, the Indian Tourism Development Corporation have built a new travellers' lodge, rather more expensive, but to international hotel standards. There is also accommodation a mile or two outside the sanctuary.

Information about the park and its wildlife is readily available at the Santi-Kutir rest house, and the guides are intelligent and helpful. The guides also provide water transport in the form of flat-bottomed boats of varying sizes, so that visits to the lake colonies can be arranged at a moment's notice for individuals or groups. Land transport, on the other hand, is ill-organized and very expensive, so that the only reasonable alternative for a tourist without a car is to walk. It is difficult to understand why bicycles, which would be ideal, are not made available for hire.

What makes Bharatpur so valuable is the way it proclaims wildlife conservation to the general public. Most tourists, on their way from Agra to Jaipur, probably have little special interest in conservation; they may approve of it as a vague notion but are unlikely to have any active involvement. What they are guaranteed at Bharatpur, in even the shortest visit, is a spectacular bird-watching experience under ideal conditions. A visit is almost as predictable as a tour round Disneyland, and this is in no way intended to be derogatory. It is precisely what tourists want, and the surprise of most first-time visitors at the sanctuary's richness can hardly fail to raise the stock of conservation in public opinion.

UNDER THE RED SEA
Jon Kenfield

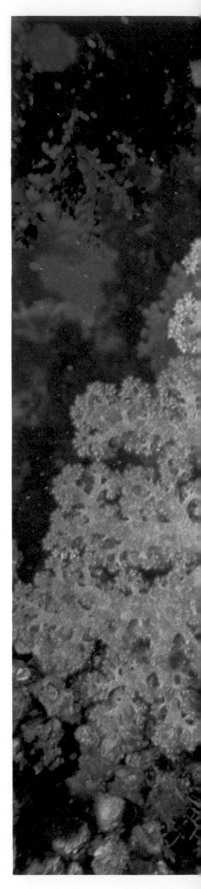

The Red Sea, the Gulf of Aqaba, the Gulf of Eilat – it all depends whose map you look at for what you'll call the narrow strip of water which so neatly divides Jordan and Saudi Arabia from Israel and the Sinai Peninsula. But whatever the name, the history and character of this unique stretch of water remains the same. It was a trade route to the east in the days of King Solomon and today 200,000-tonne oil tankers lumber along the same channels.

The Red Sea waters parted for Moses and the children of Israel and then closed in on and drowned their Egyptian pursuers: today those same waters provide a natural buffer which somehow absorbs the physical tension between Israel and two of her Arab neighbors. In Crusader times there was considerable activity here in the struggle against Saladin – the remains of a Crusader fortress may be seen at Coral Island, just a short way below Eilat, the largest and most northerly town on the Gulf.

For several hundred years, little was heard of the area and, indeed, it even failed to show on several of the maps made of that part of the world! Then, first in 1761 and again one year later, small parties of scientists began making exploratory expeditions into what had become a fabled sea. In the Danish expedition of 1761, five of the six members died on the trip. The 1762 trip contained the Swede, Peter Forsskal, one of Linnaeus's most distinguished pupils. Through his heroic efforts science began to glimpse some of the natural wonders of the area both under the water and in the rugged Sinai desert which borders on it.

General interest continued fizzing until the big explosion came in the middle of the twentieth century. With the aid of their newly developed underwater breathing apparatus, both Hans Hass and Jacques Cousteau began exploring and, even more significantly, began filming the life in and around the Red Sea and the Gulf. Indeed, it was these very efforts which have since caused so many to take up the challenge of undersea adventure. For the first time, everybody could see what went to make up one of this earth's most fascinating, yet previously impenetrable environments.

Since those pioneering days, there have been many changes. The entire western coast of the Gulf is now under Israel's control since her forces occupied the Sinai Peninsula during the Six Day War of 1967. Firstly for military purposes and secondly to promote tourism, a good road was laid from Eilat at the top of the Gulf right down the coast past Ras Muhamed at the southernmost tip and up the Gulf of Suez towards Abu Rhodes. Public accommodation has been built at several of the oases along the coast and there is a major civilian and naval settlement at Ofira (Sharm-el-Sheikh) deep in the south (mainly because it is strategically well placed to guard the entrance to the Gulf at the Straits of Tiran). Cheap charter flights to Eilat have now made this formerly remote and mysterious wilderness easily accessible to the ordinary traveller.

Remarkably consistent weather draws the usual hordes of sun-worshippers, but since these generally crowd on to just a few beaches and concentrate around the bars and restaurants in Eilat and other centers, they have little effect on the ecology of the area in general. At the same time enthusiasts

are able to take trips into the interior of the Sinai, either by jeep or camel, to see some of the very specialized flora and fauna of the desert environment.

Contrary to the popular concept of a desert, the Sinai does not consist of romantic, rolling sand-dunes. Instead, it is a place of rugged granite and harsh yellow-gray sand (mainly pulverized coral). Indeed, fossils tell us that much of its area was once under water, and was actually part of a coral sea. Furthermore, the Sinai contains many watering holes and, although extremely localized, these form a very significant feature of the desert supporting, as they do, individual but entire miniature eco-systems.

It is a remarkable place where, it would seem, nothing could survive – but the desert has not a few inhabitants. If you are in the habit of turning over stones in the heat of the day you may well disturb one of the several types of scorpion which live there. Similarly, snakes are to be found, including the poisonous asp (cure to Cleopatra's misery). A huge black beetle can be found whenever you halt for any period of time and lizards are frequently found basking in the sunlight. Moving up the evolutionary scale, there are sand-colored hares the size of northern, mountain hares. Desert foxes with small bodies but huge heads and eyes can sometimes be seen, usually by the reflection of those eyes in the beam of a car headlamp. They seem to have little instinctive fear of humans as safari members have discovered on two separate trips – one when a man awoke to find a fox licking his ear, another as a fox tried to pull his sleeping bag from under him!

Ibex may even be heard before they are seen as they climb seemingly impossible vertical rock walls, their hooves striking sharply on the rock. Breeding efforts here have so increased the stocks of this creature in the Hai-Bar nature reserve, that they have been re-introduced to areas where they had become extinct.

Bird life, near the coast at least, is also considerable – though perhaps more interesting in terms of migration than in terms of resident populations. Thus, at certain times of the year one may have the spectacular sight of dozens of vultures circling in the

thermals above the mountains which fall almost sheer to the water in many places. At the same time, normally enormously high in the air, you can spot literally thousands of buzzards on their way to or from Egypt and Africa. In one small area of mangroves forty pairs of osprey were nesting last year and I stood less than six meters from a hovering pair of these magnificent birds (inevitably, I didn't have a camera with me!). Gray and white herons are present on the shoreline almost all the year round and even spoonbills may be found. Since most of the shoreline consists of solid reef-table the only wading birds which are regularly found are those that take fish.

The largest and certainly the most enigmatic of the desert inhabitants are the Bedouins. These nomadic Arabs are still living the timeless existence that their ancestors led hundreds of years before them. Estimates of their numbers are notoriously vague, but rest at around the 6,000 figure. Although the majority are still to be found (or not found) deep in the desert with their flocks of sheep and goats, increasingly they are drifting towards the coastal shanty settlements at the oases of Nuweiba and Dahab where they spend their time fishing and tending their animals.

A strange race, Bedouins have always kept away from any real allegiance to either side in the Egypt-Israel conflict and have thus been 'tolerated' by both countries. The women and young girls do most of the work and the men have a philosophy essential to desert dwelling – time and distance have little importance to them and their fatalism is complete. Yet they are a friendly race and if you ever have a chance to sample their hospitality whilst out in the desert you will

The stonefish (left) lives up to its name, and is normally hard to spot. But beware – its spines deliver one of the most potent venoms around! It sits patiently waiting for its prey virtually to swim into its great jaws

A goby resting on coral (right). In some areas, many of the fish are so tame that they will either ignore the diver, or merely look at him curiously. At Eilat, they are used to being fed, and may give you a nip if you fail to bring food with you

A tubeworm, one of the many colorful and interesting reef inhabitants besides the fishes

The butterflyfish (above) is one of the most beautiful of all the reef fishes. By contrast, the moray eel (left) can be as ferocious as it looks: it is not advisable for a diver to extend a hand of welcome, for he will find out the hard way how sharp its teeth are and how strong its grip. Two more attractive reef fishes are the chequered hawkfish (top right) swimming beside a gorgonian coral, and an angelfish, or peacock emperor (bottom) right

find it to be as effusive as that of any dweller in a remote place.

The Government of Israel, acting through the military authorities which are directly responsible for the control of the Sinai, has declared that almost the entire coast is a nature reserve where animals must not be molested, nor fish speared, coral taken, or shellfish removed. It has even declared that the Bedouins must no longer put up the nets they used to erect at certain places along the shoreline in order to catch migrating quails which, exhausted, would drop down on to the beach just beyond the water line and so, of course, become ensnared. In return, the government provides these Arabs with other useful commodities (like nylon fishing nets) – none of which really stops them from taking fish, coral, shellfish, or quails! At least, though, the move suggests that there is an awareness of the danger to the local environment caused by the new influx of human visitors and the nature reserve authorities do work hard at trying to enforce their regulations.

If you mention to most people 'Sinai', the immediate connection is normally with Moses and his followers trooping for forty years in the wilderness. Anybody seeing the desert will sympathize with them. On the other hand, if you talk about the 'Red Sea', the very name conjures up pictures of corals with fabulous colors and shapes and of fish in impossible varieties and mixtures of form and feature. All of this would be true. Take as well the fantastic creatures which have so characterized underwater adventure since the earliest days – 15-meter-long whale sharks; tiger, hammerhead, black-tip, white-tip, and many other types of shark; giant rays and huge marine turtles; moray eels and barracuda with their fearsome teeth; squid and the very shy octopus – and it all adds up to a complete wonderland. Another world (though hardly a 'Silent World' as Cousteau called it), so different from our own that it far transcends the wildest imaginings of the most creative minds.

It's not at all essential to be a diver with full breathing apparatus to experience much of what the Red Sea can show. A trip in a glass-bottomed boat can give a good taster, while the use of a simple mask and snorkel will take you a great deal further. But if you do have SCUBA (Self Contained Underwater Breathing Apparatus) gear, you have with you the means for obtaining almost total mobility and freedom (albeit for limited periods), under the water.

Even the most graceful of divers in these waters will frequently have fish swimming up to him and looking on curiously to work out what it is that is so large and noisy and which swims so slowly and with such clumsiness! Yet in water of such clarity – you can sometimes see around forty meters horizontally – and of such warmth – never less than 21°C (the lowest temperature that coral can withstand) – it is easy to feel at ease. In fact, it is all too easy and a constant danger lies in being lured to dangerous depths to see 'just a little farther down'.

In this heady setting, by observing certain basic rules you can be fairly certain of being able to savor and observe all that is going on quite safely. Apart from the technical diving considerations it is essential always to remember that you are a visitor to this world and little more.

Already, so-called 'diver pollution' has affected some of the most accessible and well known diving sites, reducing what was once an area of beautiful coral sculptures down to a devastated expanse of broken stumps and loose rubble. Of course, with the coral gone, the habitats of many of the reef dwellers have also gone, either making them an easy prey for predators or forcing them to move from the area to seek new protection. The delicacy of the corals is such that it is absolutely essential to look and not touch: since some of the corals can give a very painful burning sting, this is also a counsel of some wisdom. There are other hidden dangers. Stone and scorpion fish are related and both have the same attitude towards life – to lie down where they can't be seen and to let their food come to them. Then, with an opening of cavernous jaws, the prey is engulfed. To aid this, the camouflage of these fish is so effective as to make them almost invisible and, as if this were not enough to protect them, they also have venomous spines on their backs which they will use as a last resort in self defense.

One observation that is very easy to make is that of the basic difference in fish behavior from place to place. In Eilat, the fish are

The curious dendrophyllia coral shows off its bright colors (right), while a clownfish nestles above a fluorescent anemone (bottom right)

(Over page) The underwater world of the Red Sea is a riot of colors and unexpected shapes. Here, a featherduster worm sways gently with the sea's quiet motion

used to divers and are used to being fed by them. Consequently, they are so bold that they may even bite you for not bringing food (since these are small fish, there is more amusement than danger in this exercise!). If you travel to an area which is very little dived in and is a nature reserve, most fish will simply ignore you or come to look at you curiously (this is a little startling when it happens to be a barracuda almost two meters in length which is hovering above your shoulder). However, if you go to an area which allows spear fishing there is a startling difference – far fewer fish are in evidence. It's extremely doubtful that this is because a significant proportion of the population has been destroyed; what has happened is that the fish have learnt to fear the appearance of a human – especially if he is making noises with his aqualung. Indeed, it may be possible to see many more creatures in such a place by using the silent snorkel.

The argument progresses beyond the localized damage that the individual or group of divers are capable of, be it from clumsiness or wantonness. For to the waters of the Gulf, and thus to the continued existence of its denizens, there are greater risks. These waters are already the most saline in the world for an open sea due to the incredible rate of evaporation in what is the fairly static mass in the north end of the Gulf. Phosphates have increased in concentration very quickly due to nearby mining operations and the resultant spillage and carriage of the dust on winds. But rearing high above all other problems is one that we know well – oil.

In 1978 alone there were two huge oil spills from the oil port which lies just outside Eilat. The largest of the two spills involved many millions of liters of oil and the slick spread over more than 25 kilometers of coastline. Only a fortunate change in wind direction prevented its doing incredible damage, and the fact that it was quite highly refined and therefore very light avoided any of it sinking below the surface of the sea. Detergents cannot be used in such places as they destroy corals at least as effectively as does the oil itself. The oil actually suffocates the coral by smothering the polyps on the living, outer surface and clogging all their respiratory and feeding mechanisms.

The unbelievable side of the cleaning-up operation was that the 'anti-pollution team' consisted of about half a dozen poorly paid Bedouins throwing straw into the water, supposedly to trap and absorb the oil. They then raked the filthy stuff on to the beach, where it lay for a long time thereafter. Protests, letters, and petitions produced only a stony silence from both oil company and officials – obviously they were too embarrassed to allow anybody's name to get involved in the whole scandalous affair.

Hopefully, whatever the outcome of the current Middle East situation, diving and tourism will continue to flourish in the Sinai and in the Gulf waters. There is so much to be seen there, so much to learn and appreciate, so much that is romantic, mysterious and unique, that it would be yet another of the desperate shames on mankind's long list if politics, industry, or human nature were allowed to do any further harm to this glorious place. As one of the purest and most concentrated examples of the power of nature, surely it's not too much to ask that it be allowed to continue to exist, unmolested, as it has done since time immemorial?

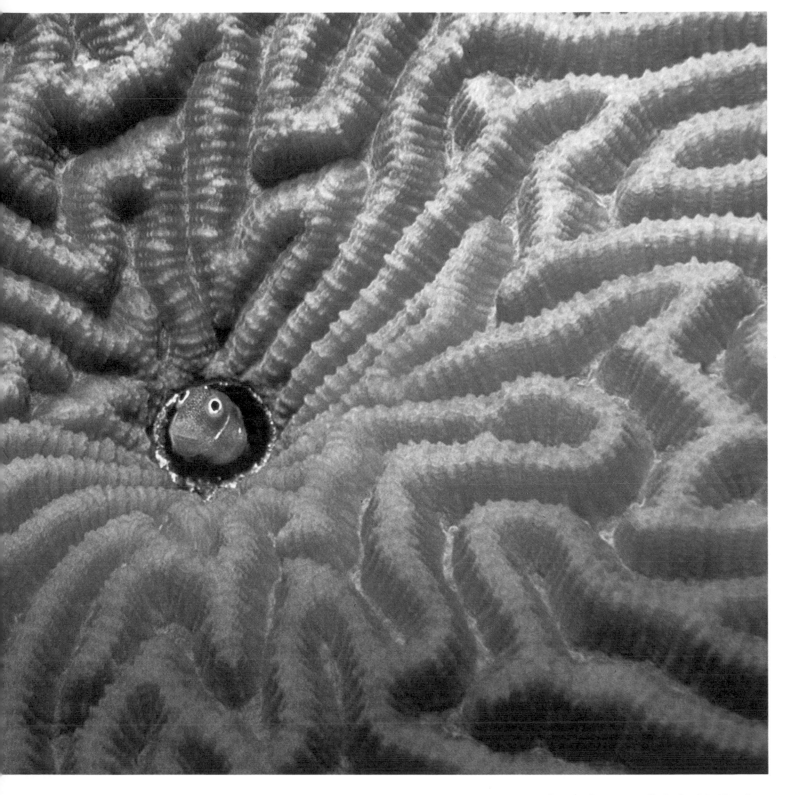

A blenny pokes cheekily out of a brain coral to eye the diver. Some places in this watery wonderland are – unfortunately – beginning to experience 'diver pollution', while like almost every other body of water, there is the added threat of oil pollution

105

THE WALRUS NEEDS HELP
Randall Reeves

At first glance the walrus is not an endearing animal. Its eyes are always bloodshot, giving it an enraged, or at least intoxicated appearance. Its bristly upper lip and pug snout are reminiscent of the mad bulldog that bit the mailman. And those ridiculous tusks – they make nuzzling seem unthinkable. Its tough, wrinkled, warty hide, constant bellowing, and remarkable stench combine to make the walrus a most *resistable* creature!

From another viewpoint, however, it is an impressive beast. Mostly we see the walrus on land or ice, where it hunkers about laboriously, as often as not jabbing the backside of its neighbor and drawing blood. But in the water the walrus is at home, moving its bulk about with the same grace and agility that mark the movements of other, sleeker members of the seal family. It inhabits shallow shelf waters where rich beds of clams and other invertebrates are only a short dive away. The walrus's eating habits are delicate, if rather gluttonous. It rips off the tender siphons and feet of its molluscan prey, leaving the shells and viscera strewn across the ocean floor. Some scientists see walruses as the marine counterparts of earthworms, disturbing the substrate and recycling vital nutrients, thereby enhancing productivity throughout the food chain.

Among its closest relatives – the sealions and seals – the walrus is unique in some important ways. Virtually all these animals are annual breeders, with mature females producing a pup every year during their prime. Walruses, though, only give birth every second or third year, almost always to a single pup. Most seals nurse for a very short period – from a few days (hooded seals) to a few weeks (monk seals) – after which the pup is abandoned by its mother. But the walrus's maternal bond is firm and prolonged. Pups nurse for a year or more and remain with their mothers for two years.

The walrus's parental solicitude did not go unnoticed by early polar explorers. Nansen, a daring yet unusually sensitive Norwegian adventurer, told of killing two pups near Franz Josef Land, off the northwest coast of Russia. As the herd dispersed and fled into the water, only the mothers of the two dead youngsters remained on the ice: 'One sniffed at its little one and nudged it, apparently unable to understand what had happened. It only saw blood streaming from its head, at which it wailed and wept like a human mother.' When Nansen attempted to retrieve his catch, the mother walrus intervened: 'She grasped the carcass of the dead cub in one of her fore-flippers and disappeared with it into the depths. The second mother repeated this maneuver.'

Walrus hunters exploited this care-giving behavior by harpooning and restraining a calf. It would emit what one hunter described as 'a peculiar, plaintive, grunting cry, eminently expressive of alarm and of a desire for assistance'. The wailing infant seldom failed to attract a detachment of well-meaning adults, who themselves became easy game for the ingenious, if ruthless, hunters.

Unfortunately the walrus has been unable either to charm northern peoples or to defend itself against them. There was, perhaps, a measure of equality between the primitive native huntsman, armed with nothing more than a stone- or ivory-tipped

lance, and the thick-skinned beast with its powerful neck and formidable tusks. But the walrus proved no match for the adventurers and profiteers who began probing its subarctic and arctic realm as early as the ninth and tenth centuries. A Norwegian expedition found walruses to be plentiful along the northwest coast of Eurasia in the ninth century and soon set upon them for ivory and leather. The tusks had great ornamental appeal, and the hides proved useful in fashioning ships' cables.

In 1603, large herds of walruses were discovered on Bear Island in the Barents Sea by English explorers. The animals displayed an astonishing naivety, allowing the hunters to walk among them, sometimes shooting, sometimes stabbing with lances, often killing hundreds within a few hours. By 1611, when William Gordon visited the island, the walruses that remained had altered their behavior and showed a pitiful fear of man:

> By no means would they [the walruses] go on those beaches and places, that formerly they have been killed on. But fortie or fiftie of them together, went into little holes within the Rocke, which were so little, steepe, and slipperie, that as soon as wee did approach towards them, they would tumble all into the sea.

This altogether understandable tendency of walruses to shun 'haul-outs' on which members of their tribe have been slain is the basis for a time-honored taboo among native walrus hunters in Hudson Bay. Fred Bruemmer, in his popular book *Encounters with Arctic Animals*, describes an incident in northern Foxe Basin, near Igloolik, in which a group of young hunters killed some walruses on an *ugli*, or land (as opposed to ice) haul-out. 'Their elders were furious. They made the young men go back, and ordered them to dump all remains of the carcasses into deep water and to wash the place of slaughter thoroughly.' Only by appeasing (or deceiving) the walruses in this manner could the elders feel confident of the walruses' return to their ancestral breeding place.

Such exemplary concern for the long-term availability of game (scientists might refer to it as 'sustainable yield') was not part of the commercial hunter's world-view. He went North not to live but to take what he could and leave. The consequences for the walrus were disastrous. Few people seem to realize that the tens of thousands that once hauled out at or near Spitsbergen were as effectively exterminated as the Greenland, or bowhead, whales in that region. James Lamont, in his book *Seasons with the Sea-Horses*, recounts what may be the most grisly slaughter on record. It occurred at one of the islands of the Spitsbergen archipelago in 1852 and involved only sixteen men armed with little more than iron spears. They crept ashore unnoticed by a huge herd of walruses and began systematically stabbing to death the animals nearest the shore. Quickly the men managed to cordon off the other animals from access to the water – 'in a manner barricaded by a wall of carcasses'. According to Lamont, the men did not lay down their spears until 900 walruses had been slain, and their small vessels could hardly begin to accommodate this immense quantity. Lamont arrived at this island six years later and found 'abundant testimony to corroborate the entire truth of the story'. The beach was strewn with flattened, rotting carcasses.

Walruses once inhabited the Gulf of St Lawrence and Sable Island (off the coast of Nova Scotia) in some numbers, but they were all but extinct south of Labrador by the end of the eighteenth century. As many as 1,500 are said to have been taken on one occasion at the Magdalen Islands, their fat rendered into oil, their hides exported to America for carriage traces and to England for glue, and their tusks sold for ornamental (and a few practical) uses. Today their effective range in the Atlantic is limited to northern Hudson Bay, the remote reaches of Foxe Basin, and northern Baffin Bay and its adjacent waters. A few hundred still exist off northeast Greenland, throughout the Spitsbergen chain, and at Franz Josef Land and Novaya Zemlya in the Soviet Arctic. A geographically isolated subspecies, the Laptev walrus, persists in the central Arctic of Russia, numbering perhaps several thousand. The only real stronghold of the species today is the area between Alaska and northeastern Siberia.

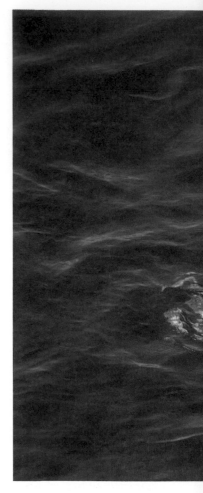

Though the walrus may seem clumsy on land, in the water it is at home and moves with the grace and agility typical of the seal family. It feeds on shellfish and other invertebrates in the shallow shelf waters, ripping off the siphons and feet of its prey, and leaving the remains scattered across the seabed

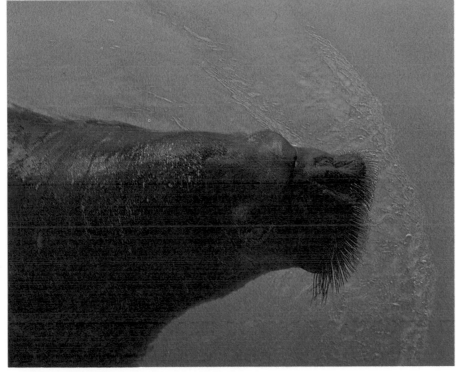

Here the Pacific walrus still flourishes – recent estimates of its total population have ranged as high as 200,000, which may be near the carrying capacity of its Bering and Chukchi seas environment.

In the absence of its most destructive enemy – man – the walrus would not live without fear. At least two formidable inhabitants of the Arctic prey upon walruses. Polar bears are probably the walrus's most serious natural adversary. According to Charleton Ray, a professor at Johns Hopkins University who has spent much of the last fifteen years studying walruses in the Bering and Chukchi seas, pups are usually the last to tumble into the water when a group of walruses is disturbed. In his view this makes them especially vulnerable, particularly during winter when access to the water is limited by ice cover. Numerous reliable accounts exist of walrus-hunting polar bears, and it is felt that in some areas they contribute significantly to the mortality rate of young animals.

The role of the killer whale as a walrus predator is less well documented. Where their ranges overlap, doubtless there is a certain degree of rivalry, and the appearance of killer whales can cause a swimming herd of walruses to scramble on the nearest available land or ice. However, the walrus is by no means a passive victim. As Richard Perry notes in his book *The World of the Walrus*: 'There is certainly one authentic record of a bull walrus, on being approached by a pack of killers when lying out on a floe, plunging into the water among them and subsequently surfacing with his tusks deep in one killer's back.'

When provoked or hungry, the walrus can itself be a fearsome predator. Seal blubber is found in walrus stomachs with surprising frequency, and some 'rogues' are believed to subsist primarily on ringed and bearded seals. But the walrus's teeth are poorly adapted for ripping and tearing warm-blooded prey, so carnivorous behavior is clearly an anomaly. Nineteenth-century British whalers sailing across the Norwegian and Greenland seas in search of bowheads sometimes saw walruses preying on narwhals. A vivid account of such behavior was provided by Robert Gray, whose father killed a bull in the process of disembowelling a fourteen-foot narwhal, whose five-foot tusk had apparently served poorly, if at all, as an implement of defense. Gray's father explained the walrus's success in this way: 'The only way I can think of is that he [the walrus] had found the narwhal asleep, gone underneath him, dug his tusks into his belly, and clasped him round the body with his flippers, in which position we found them, with this difference, that the walrus was uppermost.'

The appearance of firearms and motorized transport in the North have distorted the balance long maintained between primitive human communities and the tribes of walruses, seals, musk oxen, caribou, and polar bears on which they used to depend. Men can now claim far more than their share of these renewable resources, and local game supplies in most areas are depleted. Native hunting today is done with little regard for ancestral methods of capture or utilization. Rather than stalking and harpooning individual walruses, thereby ensuring a high rate of retrieval, most hunters in Canada and Alaska shoot indiscriminately into groups of animals hauled out on the ice, wounding many that slide into the water to die a slow and painful death. Walruses that die in the water sink almost immediately. Those that are recovered are seldom butchered and utilized as fully as they might be. Tusk ivory, valued at more than $30 (£15) a pound, is the primary objective, so 'head-hunting' is common. Scores of headless carcasses have been known to wash ashore on the Alaskan coast, a grotesque testimony to the wasteful slaughter taking place on the ice.

Few native hunters (outside the Thule district of Greenland) maintain dog teams now; they rely almost exclusively on snowmobiles or aircraft for winter transport. While the value of the ivory and the joy of hunting still lure some men to launch expeditions in their Peterhead boats or freight canoes to walrus *uglit*, the incentive to hunt walruses for dogfood is gone. Industries based on extraction of minerals and fossil fuels, military bases, political and public welfare institutions, and private commercial ventures, have sprung up throughout the North and drawn men and their families away from their traditional manner of living. In many cases this has relieved the hunting pressure on species like the walrus – but unfortunately, new threats have emerged to replace overhunting, and Arctic animals may still be in trouble.

In Canada, radar station construction is said to have caused the abandonment by walruses of at least one traditional haul-out, and there can be little doubt that the hustle and bustle accompanying northern development will continue to diminish the amount of habitat suitable for this highly specialized mammal. Ice breakers, artificial islands, tanker traffic, and pipeline construction promise to transform the walrus's icy homeland into a much busier, more polluted place than it ever was. Having retreated literally to the end of the earth, this magnificent beast no longer has a choice but to become accustomed to rubbing shoulders with modern man and his machines. Thoughtless 'head-hunting', oil spills, and harassment taken together constitute a real threat to the continued existence of some local walrus populations. In addition, the species may soon be competing directly with humans for food. The Bering Sea is known to be rich in bivalve molluscs, including clams. American soup companies, having badly depleted the clam resource off the east coast of the continent, now have designs on the rich beds known to exist off Alaska. An experimental attempt at hydraulic dredging in the Bering Sea was undertaken with government support in the summer of 1977.

The days when the frigid shores of Spitsbergen would suddenly come alive with heaps of walrus flesh are past and not likely to return in our lifetime. Yet it may not be overly optimistic to hope that the days of uncontrolled hunting, as well as mindless alteration of wildlife habitat, are themselves on the wane. At the beginning of this century perhaps a hundred northern elephant seals (the largest relative of the walrus) remained on this planet. After a long period of protection they have rebounded to almost 50,000 strong. A similar story may one day be told of the walrus – that noisy, foul-smelling, clam-grubbing, gloriously improbable work of nature's art.

Traditional pressures may not be so strong now – the walruses are no longer used to feed Eskimo dog teams (instead, oil is needed to feed the snowmobiles and aircraft). Nevertheless, hunting still takes place, and development of the Arctic has produced new conflicts between man and walrus. It remains to be seen if the two can live together in the future

THE WORLD'S BIGGEST OIL SPILL
Tony & Liz Bomford

The winter of 1978 was a bad time for seabird colonies around Britain and France. It had been a hard season with gales and continual rough weather throughout January and February. Plankton had been scarce and birds had not been able to find food as readily as usual out at sea. Puffins were particularly hit, so much so that they had not molted properly before starting their migration from the Bay of Biscay back to their breeding sites around the British Isles. Many of them could not fly well and were rafting on the surface of the water. It was unfortunate therefore that their journey northwards should coincide with that of the *Amoco Cadiz*.

European newspaper headlines told the grim story day after day throughout March and April: 'Amoco Cadiz – world's worst oil disaster', 'Supertanker grounded after steering system fails', 'Amoco captain delays calling for aid', and 'Pollution battle on Brittany's beaches'. The world reacted with horror to the news as 220,000 tons of crude oil spewed on to the attractive holiday coves of north-west France, choking all forms of life. Dead and dying birds began to be washed ashore and men in the oil industry groaned. Their worst nightmare had been realized.

Reaction was fast, but salvage experts were hampered by appalling weather conditions and by the unprecedented scale of the disaster. As the *Amoco Cadiz* was pounded into a mass of twisted metal, her vast cargo leaked into the sea, coming ashore in large thick carpets spread over 200 miles of French coastline and destroying the region's valuable shellfish and tourist industries. Contingency plans had been prepared by the authorities but not for an emergency on this scale. There were not enough trained men to organize the operation, and insufficient equipment. The oil piled up in sheltered bays forming a deep stinking brown mass. Meanwhile strong winds drove other slicks eastwards, polluting more beaches and even threatening the Channel Islands.

We arrived on the scene with a host of reporters and photographers to witness the death throes of the region. Others arrived with more practical aims. Teams of young people from all over Europe scoured the beaches and dunes for dying seabirds, and many more young volunteers took up shovels and began the gargantuan task of clearing up. Farmers left their fields to haul tractor loads of sand and seaweed away and the army moved in. Lorries plowed over the dunes, their wheels caked in oil, their windscreens opaque with the finer volatiles. Mechanical diggers, tankers, and pumps were brought but the enormity of the task defeated them.

It was a bright sunny day, the beginning of spring and the first migrant birds were arriving, but for as far as the eye could see evil-looking oil smothered the sea, the rocks, and the once golden sands. Even the air was foul and the sandhoppers that had escaped the first contamination lay dead in pale heaps choked by the oily breeze. Along the dunes bees sucked at sticky lesser celandine flowers and a chiffchaff sang from a greasy bush. There was little to celebrate.

Although 4,000 French troops had been drafted into the area, lacking special equipment they were frequently reduced to wading in the sea with plastic dustbins,

A dead puffin lies in mute witness to the 'Amoco Cadiz' oil spill, the biggest such disaster of all time

forming human chains to pass the oil back to waiting trucks. Most of the pumps available were unsuitable for use in sea water and fresh water had to be brought by tanker to hose down the rocks. Some dug trenches and shovelled the oily seaweed and sand into polythene bags for disposal. To begin with this too was a problem and the troops merely dumped the oil in pits dug in the dunes. Conservationists quickly pointed out that this action spread the pollution and so a collection plant was opened in Brest. It was hard, dispiriting work. Continually in the stench of oil, many became sick and the Red Cross stations were busy with vomiting volunteers. Many residents began to feel unwell too.

A rock pipit fluttered in display but the shoreline was dead. Even the usual roar of the sea sounded strangely muffled as the heavy oil suppressed normal wave motion. The oil was so thickly piled that the water simply could not reach the sand. One by one the bird corpses were washed ashore but they were frequently unrecognizable lying amongst the oily lumps and rotting seaweed. Teams picked their way through the morass collecting corpses. In a disaster of this sort, data on the dead is vital to safeguard the future of the living. Very little is known of seabird activities offshore in winter, and patterns of migration are only partly understood.

Occasionally a living bird turned up. These shattered survivors were taken swiftly to Brest where a bird hospital had been set up by the Société pour l'Étude et la Protection de la Nature en Bretagne. Most of the seabirds rescued after the *Torrey Canyon* disaster ten years earlier had died before being rehabilitated and little data was collected. This time new techniques developed by the British RSPCA were used. At first morale was high for it seemed more birds were surviving the rigors of captivity and cleaning, but in the end only 258 were fit to return to the sea from this center, although nearly 5,000 birds were recorded.

The pile of blackened corpses in the yard grew and a board showed that over thirty-five different species had been found. Mostly puffins, the dead included guillemots, razorbills, cormorants, and gulls. Great northern divers stretched lifeless in the makeshift

laboratory and even a kingfisher was added to the sad list. Most of the birds had simply died of shock soon after becoming badly oiled. Other birds came ashore only slightly marked, but they ingested oil while preening their feathers and then died of poisoning. Many other birds died of cold, for the oil caked their plumage and destroyed its insulating properties. The number of birds found on the shore only gives a rough idea of the size of the disaster for the seabirds, as many corpses would have disappeared at sea or remained rotting unrecognized amongst the decaying seaweed.

Dr Peter Hope Jones, representing Britain's Royal Society for the Protection of Birds, looked for bands and measured the wing length of the puffins. This varies slightly depending on the breeding site the bird has come from. He told us that birds from southern Ireland, Wales, mainland Scotland, and the Orkney and Shetland islands had been found. Ten years before, the *Torrey Canyon* had wiped out many puffin colonies and numbers have been declining ever since, almost certainly owing to increasing oil pollution at sea and the puffins' absorption of poly-chlorinated biphenyls. Known as PCBs, the latter are a product of the paint and plastics industries. After a hard winter the *Amoco Cadiz* disaster was serious indeed. The puffins' slow rate of of reproduction – they only lay one egg each year – means that recovery is very difficult. It has even been hypothesized that puffins might become extinct around British shores in the next twenty years.

Oil pollution can be accidental but it is frequently deliberate, caused by tankers and cargo ships cleaning their tanks illegally at sea. Responsible major oil companies no longer do this, but there are an enormous number of ships flying flags of convenience which do, secure in the knowledge that it is almost impossible to bring them to court. Birds such as gulls usually react to oil slicks by flying away, but puffins and the other auks respond by diving and then they frequently emerge right in the middle of the oil. The greatest danger is on major shipping routes where accidents and spillage are inevitable. The increased size of oil tankers means that accidents, when they occur, are going to be severe. The *Amoco Cadiz*, for

French troops cleaning up the beaches of Brittany in the wake of the 'Amoco Cadiz' oil spill

example, was only a medium-sized super-tanker. There are many bigger ones on the high seas.

British auks are threatened by the enormous quantity of traffic using the Channel as well as by oil-drilling activities in the North Sea and the Atlantic. Here, weather conditions are much rougher, and untried, pioneering technology is being used to extract and deliver oil to the terminals. It is highly probable that sometime soon an accident will occur in these northern waters that will wipe out the entire breeding bird population of a large site such as Noss or Hermaness in Shetland where tens of thousands of birds habitually form large rafts on the water in the springtime.

The *Amoco Cadiz* is the biggest oil disaster to date, but it may be simply the forerunner of a series of incidents and a steady increase in pollution around northern European shores that will decimate wildlife. We need oil. It is the lifeblood of western industrial society, but the conditions sur-rounding the supply of this vital commodity are alarming. International legislation is the cumbersome and unwieldy tool that con-trols shipping but it is full of anomalies and loopholes. The vast sums of money involved make oil the biggest gamble of modern times and it attracts responsible investors and dubious entrepreneurs alike. It was a combination of the rough pioneering spirit of the oil world and the archaic traditions of marine salvage that sealed the fate of the *Amoco Cadiz*

The situation brought two tough captains into direct conflict with each other. The *Amoco Cadiz* needed help but the salvage price asked represented the virtually com-plete loss of her multi-million dollar cargo. Without a salvage contract the tug captain was reluctant to endanger his own boat and the lives of his crew. Salvage in bad weather, with the boat awash, continually maneuver-ing amidst mountainous waves, is a risky business. Almost miraculously the *Amoco Cadiz* drifted twelve hours amongst the maze of tooth-like rocks off the Breton coast whilst telexes chattered the news to her owners across the Atlantic. Precious hours were lost before rescue was attempted and the inevitable happened as the ship grounded.

French authorities immediately accused

the *Amoco Cadiz* of failing to notify them of her plight although the ship's steering gear had broken down a mere six miles offshore, but the fact is that international procedures in the case of such an emergency have never been worked out. Strangely, the country to suffer seldom has jurisdiction over the ship involved. (When the oil tanker *Eleni V* went down off Britain's east coast shortly afterwards the Department of Trade spent nearly a week trying to ascertain the ship's owners.)

The *Amoco Cadiz* spilt her 220,000 tons of oil into the sea over the next few days as one by one her tanks split open. There was little that could be done about it. Roaring gales prevented effective action. It is generally agreed that standards of tanker construction should be improved, but even if the *Amoco Cadiz* had complied with the latest United Nations proposals it would not have prevented the disaster, for they call for duplication of every part of the steering except the hydraulics – precisely the system which failed. The *Amoco Cadiz* was, anyway, only four years old, and compared to most tankers, sophisticated and up-to-date. It will take many years to replace today's tanker fleet with vessels designed according to the new regulations.

It has been shown that 80 per cent of accidents at sea owe more to human error than to mechanical failure. A large part of the world's shipping is registered in countries such as Panama where regulations are lax, particularly as regards crew training. The United Nations Intergovernmental Maritime Consultative Organization (IMCO) would like to put an end to this, and has started drafting legislation on marine safety and pollution. But it takes several years for legislation to be passed by the parliaments and assemblies of the various member countries, and still longer for these laws to become effective. In the meantime, the pressure on the environment grows.

Frustrated by IMCO's lack of speed and alarmed by tanker spills in American waters, President Carter threatened unilateral action in 1977 to enforce tough new standards on ships using US ports. IMCO members dissuaded him from this course, but as the *Amoco Cadiz* incident shows, the international community must act more quickly to push through marine legislation. Govern-

The big clean-up under way. Complacent governments toy with the problem of oil pollution, but perhaps they would develop a greater sense of urgency if politicians were obliged to spend time on the beaches scooping up the mess with a plastic bucket

ments need the authority to control vessels and their cargoes if they threaten the environment, and traffic regulations in congested areas like the Channel need to be rigorously enforced. The British government's Advisory Committee on Oil Pollution of the Sea reported a rise from 500 oil spills in 1975 to 642 in 1977. Clearly these are not matters for lengthy debate and delay.

Most countries are totally unprepared for disaster on the scale of the *Amoco Cadiz*. Yet one can stand on the shores of Brittany watching ship after ship of this size and bigger passing but a few miles off Ushant. The technology to deal with oil spillage is growing but it seems unco-ordinated. Contingency plans remain woefully inadequate. The *Torrey Canyon* disaster highlighted the need to be prepared with low toxicity dispersants – but a decade later the French repeated the same mistakes, damaging much marine life with highly toxic detergents. And there was only enough of them to treat a fraction of the oil spilled and nowhere near enough ancillary equipment to go round. Absorbants such as chalk, crumbled peat, and powdered rubber intended to sink the oil merely created a sludge that was harder to clear up than the oil alone. In Britain dispersants used on the *Eleni V* spill a few weeks later were almost useless, for the oil turned out to be a grade that should never have been treated at all. It seems that while some effort has been made in the last decade to come to terms with oil spillage the technology is still experimental and insufficient.

Responsibility does not lie simply with the companies that transport the oil. To a large extent they are cast in a role created for them by the governments demanding increased industrialization and a society requiring comfort and convenience. All oil-consuming countries must shoulder responsibility for the environment by ensuring that adequate legislation is speedily passed and enforced and that funds are available for research and to carry out emergency cleansing operations when required.

It is deplorable that the reaction of many ships' captains in the Channel at the time of the *Amoco Cadiz* disaster was to take advantage of the catastrophe by illegally cleaning their tanks at sea, aggravating an already grave situation. Many birds washed up in the Channel Islands were killed by quite different types of oil to that carried by the *Amoco Cadiz*. However, while complacent governments toy with the problems to the extent that a third of these busy shipping lanes remain inadequately surveyed, it is hard to know where to throw the first stone.

As consumers we are all involved. We are faced with pollution of the environment on a vast and potentially irreversible scale. Sophisticated technology has not made us masters of our own destiny but simply magnified the consequences of human error. If our political leaders and captains of industry were to spend an eight-hour shift wading in the sea, scooping up oil with a plastic bucket, we might look forward to some real changes.

KRILL FOR ALL—OR FREE FOR ALL?

David Stonegate

Housewives have long been accustomed to the steadily rising price of meat. More recently they have found that fish, too, has been accounting for a rising proportion of the family food budget. Some of this rise in price has been due to the familiar effects of inflation – but an increasingly important factor has been the growing scarcity of supplies. If the housewife finds time to read a newspaper in between efforts to balance her budget, she will be aware that one kind of fish after another has been over-harvested – which explains why it has vanished from the shops.

The world demand for protein is increasing, and conventional supplies of meat and fish seem unable to cope. What is the answer? Should we all become vegetarians? Maybe that would be a good answer: it would certainly be less wasteful of Planet Earth's resources (Britain, for example, which currently imports half her food, could probably be self-sufficient if her inhabitants converted to a predominantly vegetarian diet, with only a small amount of animal protein for variety).

It is unlikely, however, that a vegetarian regime is upon us just yet – instead, we may all be eating a large shrimp called krill. Living in the southern oceans around Antarctica, krill is found in huge concentrations and seems destined to become one of the world's greatest protein resources. So great is its potential, in fact, that it may be possible (according to United Nations estimates) to harvest it indefinitely at a rate equal to the current global fish catch. This means an annual haul of some seventy million tons of krill. Not only is krill plentiful, it is also extremely rich in protein. Australian and Argentinian scientists have estimated that a catch of this magnitude could provide 1,000 million people (or a quarter of the world's population) with just over half an ounce of protein a day. Put another way, one ounce of krill contains the same amount of protein as one and a quarter pounds of beefsteak.

Krill is the most important element in the Antarctic marine ecosystem, which is surprisingly productive. (While there are several species of zooplankton which are known collectively as 'krill', the most numerous is *Euphausia superba*, a shrimp about the length of a man's thumb.) Though circumpolar in distribution, there appear to be several areas of concentration corresponding to eddies in oceanic circulation. Interestingly, catches of whales in these areas have always been higher than elsewhere (whales feed on krill).

Krill spawn mainly between January and March. The eggs are released at the surface, sink to the lower levels of warm, deep water, hatch, and develop as they rise to the surface. During the next two to three years they grow to a length of about two and a half inches, and are found mainly in the upper 600 feet of water. The Antarctic krill gather in the summer months in dense swarms, often several hundred yards across, in which the crustaceans may be highly concentrated. It appears that mature krill undertake daily vertical migrations, rising to the surface and dispersing when feeding actively. When they stop feeding they form the swarms and then descend perhaps 250 feet. It has been estimated that the total weight of Antarctic krill may range from

Antarctic krill. The lure of a huge new source of protein is attracting fishermen of many nations to the chill waters of the Southern Ocean where they hope to scoop up millions of tons of the thumb-sized crustaceans

118

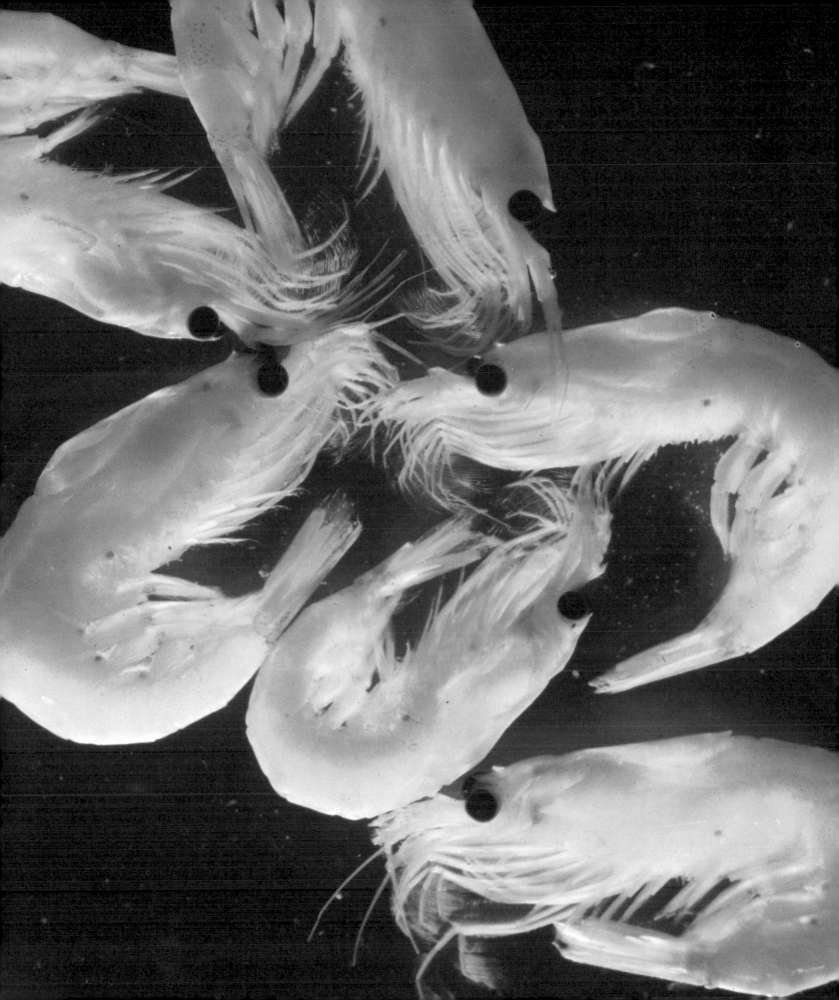

650 million tons to as high as 1,200 million tons at the peak of the breeding season.

Cephalopods, mainly the oceanic squids, form another important group of invertebrate animals in Antarctic waters. There may be about twenty species occurring in large numbers – and they are major consumers of krill. Very little is known about these squids, though the annual consumption of them by whales, seals, and birds probably amounts to about twenty million tons. But even this amount of squids would in turn consume about 100 million tons of krill.

In contrast to other oceans, the Southern Ocean does not contain dense shoals of pelagic fish. Some small species may be abundant in the open ocean, but because they do not form concentrations a fishery is not likely to develop; probably only fish that live near the coast and island groups are of commercial importance. Nevertheless, the fish also feed on krill.

The Antarctic birds are major consumers of krill. Of the forty-four breeding species, twenty-five are petrels and albatrosses and seven are penguins. Between them, these birds eat at least twenty million tons of krill, eight million tons of squid, and eight million tons of fish. The penguins take 90 per cent of this – and at South Georgia alone it has been estimated that macaroni and gentoo penguin chicks consume a million tons of krill in two to three months.

There are some seventeen million seals in the Antarctic (including the crabeater seal, the world's most numerous) and together they eat about sixty-nine million tons of krill every year (50 per cent more than the current consumption by whales), six million tons of squid, and eight million tons of fish.

Five species of migratory baleen whales appear in Antarctic waters during the summer, where they feed on krill. (One large toothed whale, the sperm whale, is also found there, but it is only the males which enter the Antarctic to feed on squid and fish.) The large baleen whales feed intensively in Antarctica during the summer, when they store up energy in the form of blubber. In the autumn they migrate northwards to breed in tropical and sub-tropical waters. In the winter they feed at only a tenth of the summer rate, and then migrate southwards again in the spring.

The baleen whales have been hunted since 1904, when their numbers were slightly over one million; they probably consumed five million tons of fish, twelve million tons of squid – and 190 million tons of krill. By 1973 their numbers had been reduced through over-hunting to about half a million, eating 130,000 tons of fish, five million tons of squid, and forty-three million tons of krill. Besides being reduced in number, the whales have also been reduced in size, as historically the whaling industry has preferred to take the largest animals, only moving on to hunt the smaller species when the bigger ones became scarce. This accounts for the relatively greater drop in their food consumption compared with their actual numbers.

This enormous reduction in whale numbers and size means that some 150 million tons of krill formerly eaten by them could be available to the remaining whales – and to other predators. It is this surplus which man now has his eye on.

For years scientists have speculated about krill as a potential food source, but until the 1970s only the Russians seemed to take the matter seriously. In 1964 the oceanographic vessel *Akademik Knipovich* sailed into the Antarctic to catch krill, and then in 1970 the Russians began marketing 'Koral' – krill butter and krill cheese – and 'Ocean' krill paste ('in food value and flavor quality . . . similar to shrimp'). The paste is used to enrich meat pies, fish balls, salads, paté, and devilled eggs. Those who have tried it say that krill tastes like shrimp or crayfish, with perhaps a somewhat more 'concentrated' flavor than other better known crustaceans.

The Russians also claim that krill paste possesses medicinal properties. They report a 60 per cent increase in the cure rate among stomach ulcer patients treated with krill paste. Favorable effects have also been noted with such ailments as heart disease.

The Japanese, meanwhile, are testing krill in frozen fishcakes and dumplings, as a liquid protein for use in snack foods, soups, and pet foods, and as a protein concentrate. Japanese researchers suggest adding the concentrate to bread, spaghetti, Indian chapatis, Mexican tortillas – in fact, as an

Krill are eaten by many creatures, including the great whales, squid, birds, and fish; these fish (above) live around South Georgia. If man starts to take krill in massive quantities the balance of the Antarctic ecosystem could easily collapse, with unknown consequences

A flock of blue-eyed shags (right) near Signy Island, Antarctica

Three studies of Antarctic wildlife. A king penguin swims with ease beneath the surface, while a wandering albatross glides effortlessly above the sea.

A group of Adelie penguins (right) share an ice floe with a leopard seal. In an attempt to reduce the possibility of catastrophe for animals like these (which might result from uncontrolled harvesting of krill) the thirteen Antarctic Treaty Nations are working out a regime for future exploitation. It remains to be seen if this will succeed. The UN has estimated that it should be possible to harvest krill at a rate equal to the current global fish catch

all-round supplement for carbohydrate foods.

Besides the Russians and the Japanese, other nations already active in Antarctic waters include Poland (her trawlers have been hauling krill since 1972), Chile, Norway, Taiwan, South Korea, East and West Germany, and Argentina – which could become a major consumer and exporter of krill in the next few years. The largest concentrations are located in Antarctic waters claimed by Argentina, only three days' sailing from Ushuaia, the southernmost port in the country.

Of course, man is not the best krill catcher. The whales do a much better job locating them, and can scoop as much as a ton in a mouthful. Nevertheless, the fishermen are learning fast and the krill swarms are now being located with echo-sounding equipment and caught with nets, filter devices, and giant vacuum pumps which suck the krill directly aboard. The race is on, and unfettered (up to now) by international agreements the world's fishing nations are gearing up for intensive commercial harvesting of krill – lured by a huge market, potential profits, and the fact that starving people need krill.

But this bounty is not inexhaustible. The central position of krill in the Antarctic ecosystem is clear, and so are the dangers of its uncontrolled exploitation, which could wreak havoc in the southern oceans. Total catches had reached perhaps 100,000 tons a year by 1977–8, and are likely to increase rapidly over the next decade. If this harvest is not controlled a point will be reached – and it is not yet known where this point may be – when man as a competitor will begin to affect the populations of squid, fish, birds, seals, and whales. If the process were to continue unchecked there would be a serious danger of the whole system breaking down, with untold and unknown consequences for the marine life and indeed for man himself.

Aware of the stakes, the thirteen Antarctic Treaty nations are holding a series of meetings aimed at hammering out an international agreement on management of krill. This will probably be rather different from most fishing conventions. Instead of setting maximum limits for individual fishing stocks, the agreement will take account of the overall relationship between the different species in Antarctic waters; a formula will be worked out to allow the maximum sustainable yield of the entire biomass instead of a single fish species. The idea will be to provide for preservation of the delicate Antarctic ecosystem by insisting on the prevention of irreversible changes in fish populations; restoration of depleted species such as whales; and finding out more about krill and its relationship to the Antarctic environment.

The Antarctic Treaty members, mostly developed nations, have been criticized for concentrating only on conservation, and not becoming involved in the thorny question of who shall share in this harvest. Until now the countries which were not party to the Antarctic Treaty were not particularly concerned. But now that they have reason to take an interest, they may find themselves shut out from the krill fishery.

However, regardless of who does exploit this resource, it is vitally important that it should be done in a controlled and responsible manner based on the fullest possible knowledge and understanding of what makes the southern oceans tick.

WORLD WILLDLIFE FUND ADDRESSES

Headquarters

World Wildlife Fund
1110 Morges, Switzerland
Tel: (021) 71 96 11
Cable: Panda Morges
Telex: 25999 PANDA CH

National Organizations

1. WWF-Austria
(Oesterreichischer Stifterverband
für Naturschutz)
Festgasse 17, Postfach 1
1162 Vienna
Tel: (0222) 46 14 63

2. WWF-Belgium
937 Chaussée de Waterloo B5
1180 Bruxelles
Tel: (02) 375 3498

3. WWF-Canada
60 St. Clair Av. East
Suite 201
Toronto, Ontario M4T 1N5
Tel: (416) 923 8173

4. WWF-Denmark
(Verdensnaturfonden)
H C Andersens Blvd 31
1553 Copenhagen V
Tel: (01) 13 20 33

5. WWF-Finland
(Maailman Luonnon Säätiö
Suomen Rahasto)
Hanuripolku 4
00420 Helsinki 42
Tel: 532 542

6. WWF-France
(Association Française du Fonds
Mondial Pour la Nature)
23 rue d'Anjou
Paris 8e
Tel: (01) 265 0274

7. WWF-Germany
(Umweltstiftung
WWF-Deutschland)
Myliusstrasse 25
D-6000 Frankfurt am Main 1
Tel: (0611) 72 51 55

8. WWF-India
Great Western Building
1st Floor
S. Bhagat Singh Road
Bombay 400023
Tel: 292891
Cable: Pandafund Bombay

9. WWF-Italy
(Associazione Italiana per
il World Wildlife Fund)
Via P.A. Micheli 50
Rome 00197
Tel: (06) 80 20 08

10. WWF-Japan
5F Yamaki Building
Sotokanda 4-8-2
Chiyoda-Ku
Tokyo 101
Tel: (03) 255 3770

11. WWF-Kenya
PO Box 40075
Nairobi
Tel: Karon 2500

12. WWF-Luxembourg
Musée d'Histoire Naturelle
Marché aux Poissons
Luxembourg
Tel: 47 87 20

13. WWF Malaysia
PO Box 769
Kuala Lumpur
Tel: (03) 945777

14. WWF-Netherlands
(Wereld Natuur Fonds)
Postbus 7
Zeist
Tel: (03404) 29324
Cable: Wereld Natuur Fonds Zeist

15. WWF-New Zealand
PO Box 12-200
Wellington North
Tel: 735022

16. WWF-Norway
(Verdens Villmarksfond)
Mollergt. 24
Oslo 1
Tel: (02) 42 43 15

17. WWF-Pakistan
PO Box 1312
Lahore
Tel: 353062

18. WWF-Peru
(Pro Defensa de la
Naturaleza – PRODENA)
Pasaje Los Pinos 156
Galerias El Comodore Alfredo Benavides
Miraflores
Lima 18
Tel: 234507

19. WWF-South Africa
(The S.A. Nature Foundation)
PO Box 456
Stellenbosch 7600
Tel: 5025-5073

20. WWF-Spain
(Associacion para la Defensa
de la Naturaleza – ADENA)
6 Joaquin Garcia Morato
Madrid 10
Tel: (01) 410 2401/02

21. WWF-Sweden
(Världsnaturfonden)
Fituna
140 41 Sorunda
Tel: (0753) 44143
Stockholm Office:
Stureplan 3, Stockholm
Tel: (08) 22 05 00

22. WWF-Switzerland
(Stiftung WWF Schweiz)
Postfach
8037 Zürich
Tel: (01) 44 20 44

23. WWF-Turkey
(Türkiye'de Dogayi Koruma Vakfi)
Cumhuriyet Caddesi 107/4
Elmadag-Istanbul
Tel: 40 87 75

24. WWF-United Kingdom
29 Greville Street
London EC1N 8AX
Tel: (01) 404 5691

25. WWF-United States
(World Wildlife Fund Inc)
1601 Connecticut Ave. NW
Washington DC 20009
Tel: (202) 387 0800

26. WWF-Venezuela
(Fundacion para la Defensa
de la Naturaleza – FUDENA)
Apartado de Correo 70376
Caracas 107
Tel: 356800

INDEX